Quadratic Equations and Curves

Second Edition

Quadratic Equations and Curves

Second Edition

Leon J. Ablon   Sherry Blackman   Helen B. Siner
The College of Staten Island, City University of New York

Anthony Giangrasso
La Guardia Community College, City University of New York

The Benjamin/Cummings Publishing Company, Inc.
Menlo Park, California • Reading, Massachusetts
London • Amsterdam • Don Mills, Ontario • Sydney

Sponsoring Editor: Susan A. Newman
Production Editor: Madeleine Dreyfack
Book Designer: Madeleine Dreyfack
Cover Designer: Judith Sager

TO

Fannie and Meyer Ablon
Boris Kunda
Susan Elizabeth Giangrasso
Sylvia Chandler

Library of Congress Cataloging in Publication Data
Main entry under title:

Quadratic equations and curves.
 (Series in mathematics modules; module 5)
  1. Equations, Quadratic. 2. Algebra—Graphic methods.
I. Ablon, Leon J. II. Series.
QA39.2.S47 no. 5, 1980 [QA215] 512.9s [512.9'42]
ISBN 0-8053-0135-6   80-24969

ABCDEFGHIJK-DO-89876543210

The Benjamin/Cummings Publishing Company, Inc.
2727 Sand Hill Road
Menlo Park, California 94025

Preface

Purpose of the Steps in Mathematics Modules

This book is one of the Steps in Mathematics Modules. The purpose of this series is to demystify mathematics and provide a foundation for the study of college algebra. Throughout our years of teaching we have become sensitive to the difficulties our students encounter in their mathematics courses. These modules incorporate the techniques we have evolved to overcome these problems.

Features

Development of Concepts: There are very few "rules" in these texts. Whenever possible, we encourage students to figure out what to do from the meaning of the symbols.

Writing Style: We have been as clear as possible in presenting each mathematical concept. We have found that students relate well to our use of everyday language. Our guiding principle has been to use language and syntax no more complex than is necessary to convey each concept. It is the kind of language that is used in the classroom, but is rarely found in mathematics textbooks.

Organization: Each module is divided into eight lessons. Each lesson is designed to be covered in one class period.

Examples and Exercises: We have used many "worked out" examples in each lesson to demonstrate the mathematics. Each lesson ends with two sets of *graded* exercises. The first set is followed immediately by handwritten solutions, so the student can see what a typical solution might look like. The second set, or "additional" exercise set, does not have solutions in the module. The answers to these exercises can be found in the Rationale, a supplement to these modules.

How to Use the Modules

Pacing: Each module is made up of eight lessons, and contains material sufficient for a 40 to 50-minute class period. The background of some students may, of course, dictate a slower or faster pace. On the average we have found that each module can be completed in 10 to 12 class meetings, including time for review and examination.

Planning a Syllabus for a Lecture Mode: The chart below may assist you in setting up a program for a term. It shows the number of modules that can be covered in 10, 12 and 14-week terms with classes that meet 3, 4 and 5 times a week.

Weeks per term	Meetings per week		
	3	4	5
10	3 modules	3 or 4 modules	4 or 5 modules
12	3 modules	4 modules	5 modules
14	4 modules	5 modules	6 or 7 modules

Self-Study or Lab Mode of Instruction: The modules can be used in math lab or for independent study. The preceding chart serves as a guide for students to gauge their progress.

Flexibility: The modular presentation of material allows for flexibility in teaching. In particular, the concept of changing the form of expressions (Modules 2 and 4) is separated from the concept of solving equations (Modules 3 and 5).

A chart of the modules interdependence can be found in the Rationale. We recommend that each module be studied from cover to cover. This gives students a feeling of completeness and insures that they are prepared for succeeding modules.

The Diagnostic Test included in the Rationale is designed to assist in determining an appropriate starting module for each student.

Improvements in This Edition

The first edition of these modules has been used successfully by us and many other math teachers in classrooms and labs for over eight years. As a result of our experiences and helpful feedback from other teachers, we have made several changes and refinements in this second edition.

> **Decimals:** This new edition integrates a review of decimals into both the lessons and homework exercises.

> **Word Problems:** Word problems have been carefully integrated throughout the modules in the examples and exercises.

> **Exercises:** We have increased the number of homework exercises by 20%.

> **Geometry:** The series now includes a review of the concepts of perimeter, area, formulas and the Pythagorean theorem.

> **Design and Appearance:** The modules are typeset, a pleasant change from the camera-ready typewriter version of the first edition. The use of italic and boldface type enables the student to quickly pick out examples, important concepts and key terms.

The Steps in Mathematics Modules Series

The first five steps in mathematics are the equivalent of an elementary algebra course: They are:

> **Module 1**—Operations on Numbers

> **Module 2**—Operations on Polynomials

> **Module 3**—Linear Equations and Lines

> **Module 4**—Factoring and Operations on Algebraic Fractions

> **Module 5**—Quadratic Equations and Curves

> **Program Rationale and Tests**—an instructor's supplement which contains a brief description of the content of each lesson, answers to the Additional Exercises, diagnostic placement examinations and three mastery tests for each of the five modules.

Additional modules in the **Steps in Mathematics Series** cover topics in intermediate algebra and other specialized topics.

Module 1a—Practical Mathematics

Module 2a—Practical Mathematics

Module 6 —Basic Trigonometry, second edition

Module 7 —Trigonometry with Applications

Module 8 —Exponents and Logarithms

Module 9 —Advanced Algebraic Techniques

Module 10—Functions and Word Problems

Module 11—Graphing Functions

Module M —Medical Dosage Calculations, second edition

Module SI—Metric System

Acknowledgements

We wish to thank all the people who contributed to the revision of Modules 1–5 with special thanks to our reviewers:

Dr. George Bergman, University of California, Berkeley
Dr. Una Bray, Marymount Manhattan College
Professor Ruth Dorsett, Atlanta Junior College
Dr. Susan Lawrence, New York University
Dr. Betty Philips, Michigan State University
Professor Michael Shaughnessy, Oregon State University
Professor Billie J. Stacey, Sinclair Community College

Our appreciation, also, to Susan Newman, sponsoring editor, and Madeleine Dreyfack, production editor and designer. The special efforts they made to translate our ideas into a finished work are greatly appreciated.

Leon J. Ablon
Sherry Blackman
Anthony P. Giangrasso
Helen B. Siner
October, 1980

To the Student

Read this text. It was written with the help of our students so students could read it. Our students tell us that the best way to learn this material is:

1. Read the lesson.
2. Work out each EXAMPLE yourself.
3. Try the first set of EXERCISES at the end of the lesson and compare your answers with ours.
4. Do the ADDITIONAL EXERCISES for more practice.

We wish you success, and we would like to hear your reactions to the text and your suggestions for future editions.

Contents

A Look at Numbers— Some Old, Some New

In this lesson we will go back and look at the different kinds of numbers we have been working with. Then we will look at a new kind of number.

Natural Numbers

The counting numbers 1, 2, 3, 4, 5, 6, 7, 8, 9, 10, 11, 12, 13, 14 and so on are called the **natural numbers**.

Integers

The numbers $\begin{cases} 1, 2, 3, 4, 5, 6, 7 \text{ and so on} \\ 0, \\ -1, -2, -3, -4, -5, -6, -7 \text{ and so on} \end{cases}$ are called the **integers**. Notice that every natural number is also an integer.

Rational Numbers

Any number that can be written as an integer divided by another integer

$$\frac{\text{integer}}{\text{integer}}$$

is called a **rational number**. Note: The bottom integer of a rational number can never be 0 since we cannot divide by 0. Here are some rational numbers.

$$\frac{1}{2}, \quad \frac{3}{7}, \quad \frac{-2}{5}, \quad \frac{17}{4}, \quad \frac{21}{-8}, \quad \frac{-7}{3}$$

Here are some more rational numbers.

5 is rational since it can be written as $\dfrac{5}{1}$

-2 is rational since it can be written as $\dfrac{-2}{1}$

0 is rational since it can be written as $\dfrac{0}{1}$

1776 is rational since it can be written as $\dfrac{1776}{1}$

In fact, every integer is also a rational number because every integer can be written as $\dfrac{\text{integer}}{1}$. Here are more rational numbers.

$3\dfrac{1}{2}$ is rational since it can be written as $\dfrac{7}{2}$

0.013 is rational since it can be written as $\dfrac{13}{1000}$

1.7 is rational since it can be written as $1\dfrac{7}{10}$ or $\dfrac{17}{10}$

In fact, all the numbers we have worked with so far are rational numbers.

Irrational Numbers

There are numbers that are not rational numbers. They are called **irrational numbers**. We have not worked with these numbers yet, but we will do so before the end of this lesson.

Real Numbers

The rational and irrational numbers together are called the **real numbers**. The following illustration shows how a few typical rational numbers are related. After we finish the next section we will be able to include some irrational numbers in the illustration.

Real Numbers

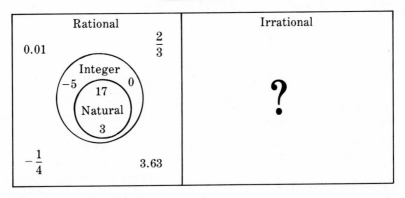

Now let's see where some of the irrational numbers come from. We'll start by squaring some numbers.

$$0^2 = 0 \cdot 0 \quad \text{or} \quad 0$$
$$1^2 = 1 \cdot 1 \quad \text{or} \quad 1$$
$$2^2 = 2 \cdot 2 \quad \text{or} \quad 4$$
$$3^2 = 3 \cdot 3 \quad \text{or} \quad 9$$
$$4^2 = 4 \cdot 4 \quad \text{or} \quad 16$$
$$5^2 = 5 \cdot 5 \quad \text{or} \quad 25$$

Now let's go in the opposite direction, that is, let's "unsquare" some numbers. The symbol for "unsquare" is $\sqrt{\ }$ which we read as "the square root of." So we read $\sqrt{25}$ as "the square root of 25."

$$\sqrt{25} = \sqrt{5 \cdot 5} \quad \text{which is} \quad 5$$
$$\sqrt{16} = \sqrt{4 \cdot 4} \quad \text{which is} \quad 4$$
$$\sqrt{9} = \sqrt{3 \cdot 3} \quad \text{which is} \quad 3$$
$$\sqrt{4} = \sqrt{2 \cdot 2} \quad \text{which is} \quad 2$$
$$\sqrt{1} = \sqrt{1 \cdot 1} \quad \text{which is} \quad 1$$
$$\sqrt{0} = \sqrt{0 \cdot 0} \quad \text{which is} \quad 0$$

Note: $(-3)^2 = (-3)(-3)$ which is 9
$(+3)^2 = (+3)(+3)$ which is 9

So there are two numbers whose square is 9; they are 3 and -3. But the symbol $\sqrt{9}$ always means the <u>positive</u> number whose square is 9. So $\sqrt{9} = 3$.

EXAMPLE 1 Simplify $\sqrt{49}$.

$$\sqrt{49} = \sqrt{7 \cdot 7} \text{ which is } 7$$

To check: $7^2 = 7 \cdot 7$ or 49.

EXAMPLE 2 Simplify $\sqrt{100}$.

$$\sqrt{100} = \sqrt{10 \cdot 10} \text{ which is } 10$$

To check: $(10)^2 = 10 \cdot 10$ or 100.

EXAMPLE 3 Simplify $\sqrt{\dfrac{1}{9}}$.

$$\sqrt{\frac{1}{9}} = \sqrt{\frac{1}{3} \cdot \frac{1}{3}} \quad \text{or} \quad \frac{1}{3}$$

To check: $\left(\dfrac{1}{3}\right)^2 = \dfrac{1}{3} \cdot \dfrac{1}{3}$ which is $\dfrac{1}{9}$.

EXAMPLE 4 Simplify $\sqrt{\dfrac{25}{16}}$.

$$\sqrt{\frac{25}{16}} = \sqrt{\frac{5}{4} \cdot \frac{5}{4}} \quad \text{or} \quad \frac{5}{4}$$

To check: $\left(\dfrac{5}{4}\right)^2 = \dfrac{5}{4} \cdot \dfrac{5}{4}$ which is $\dfrac{25}{16}$.

EXAMPLE 5 Simplify $\sqrt{0.25}$.

$$\sqrt{0.25} = \sqrt{(0.5)(0.5)} \text{ or } 0.5$$

To check: $(0.5)^2 = (0.5)(0.5) = 0.25.$

In the previous examples we found the square root of numbers like 4, 9, 16, 25, $\dfrac{1}{9}$ and 0.25. These numbers are called **perfect squares** because their square roots are rational numbers. Now let's look at the square root of a number that is not a perfect square.

Let's look at $\sqrt{5}$. The number we are looking for is not 2, because

$2^2 = 4$ which is smaller than 5

The number we are looking for is not 3, because

$3^2 = 9$ which is larger than 5

So the number we are looking for is between 2 and 3. Let's try 2.5.

$(2.5)^2$ is 6.25 which is larger than 5

So now the number we are looking for is between 2 and 2.5.

We might be tempted to try other rational numbers like 2.2, 2.3, or 2.25 but they wouldn't work either. It would be closer but still not exact. In fact, there is <u>no</u> rational number that we can multiply by itself to get 5. So the number we multiply by itself to get 5 is **irrational**. The way we write it is $\sqrt{5}$. So $\sqrt{5} \cdot \sqrt{5}$ is 5.

The following illustration shows different kinds of real numbers and how they are related. This time we include a few typical irrational numbers as well as some rational numbers.

<u>Real Numbers</u>

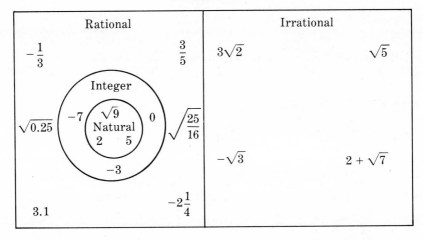

EXAMPLE 6   Simplify the following numbers.

$\sqrt{1}$	is $\sqrt{1 \cdot 1}$ or 1	(rational)
$\sqrt{2}$	cannot be simplified	(irrational)
$\sqrt{3}$	cannot be simplified	(irrational)
$\sqrt{4}$	is $\sqrt{2 \cdot 2}$ or 2	(rational)
$\sqrt{5}$	cannot be simplified	(irrational)
$\sqrt{6}$	cannot be simplified	(irrational)
$\sqrt{7}$	cannot be simplified	(irrational)

To simplify the square roots of larger numbers we need to work with them in another way. Let's look at $\sqrt{36}$, which we already know is 6.

First split 36 into $2 \cdot 2 \cdot 3 \cdot 3$. So $\sqrt{36}$ is $\sqrt{2 \cdot 2 \cdot 3 \cdot 3}$. Remember that

$$\sqrt{2 \cdot 2} \text{ is } 2$$

and $\sqrt{3 \cdot 3}$ is 3

So $\sqrt{2 \cdot 2 \cdot 3 \cdot 3}$ is $2 \cdot 3$ or 6.

EXAMPLE 7   Simplify $\sqrt{18}$.

First split 18 into primes.

$$\sqrt{18} = \sqrt{2 \cdot 3 \cdot 3}$$

Remember, $\sqrt{3 \cdot 3}$ is 3.
So $\sqrt{2 \cdot 3 \cdot 3}$ is $3 \cdot \sqrt{2}$.
We usually leave out the dot and write $3 \cdot \sqrt{2}$ as $3\sqrt{2}$.
So $\sqrt{18}$ is $3\sqrt{2}$.

EXAMPLE 8   Simplify $\sqrt{12}$.

First split 12 into primes.

$$\sqrt{12} = \sqrt{2 \cdot 2 \cdot 3}$$

Remember, $\sqrt{2 \cdot 2}$ is 2.
So $\sqrt{2 \cdot 2 \cdot 3}$ is $2\sqrt{3}$ and $\sqrt{12} = 2\sqrt{3}$.

EXAMPLE 9   Simplify $\sqrt{50}$.

$$\sqrt{50} = \sqrt{2 \cdot 5 \cdot 5}$$

which is $5\sqrt{2}$.

EXAMPLE 10   Now let's continue the list of numbers we started in example 6.

$\sqrt{8}$ is $\sqrt{2 \cdot 2 \cdot 2}$ which is $2\sqrt{2}$ (irrational)
$\sqrt{9}$ is $\sqrt{3 \cdot 3}$ which is 3   (rational)
$\sqrt{10}$ cannot be simplified   (irrational)
$\sqrt{11}$ cannot be simplified   (irrational)
$\sqrt{12}$ is $\sqrt{2 \cdot 2 \cdot 3}$ which is $2\sqrt{3}$ (irrational)
$\sqrt{13}$ cannot be simplified   (irrational)
$\sqrt{14}$ cannot be simplified   (irrational)
$\sqrt{15}$ cannot be simplified   (irrational)
$\sqrt{16}$ is $\sqrt{4 \cdot 4}$ or 4   (rational)
$\sqrt{17}$ cannot be simplified   (irrational)

This list goes on forever. Let's try some larger numbers.

EXAMPLE 11   Simplify $\sqrt{200}$.

$$\sqrt{200} = \sqrt{2 \cdot 2 \cdot 2 \cdot 5 \cdot 5}$$

which is $2 \cdot 5\sqrt{2}$ or $10\sqrt{2}$

So $\sqrt{200}$ is $10\sqrt{2}$.

EXAMPLE 12   Simplify $\sqrt{28}$.

$$\sqrt{28} = \sqrt{2 \cdot 2 \cdot 7}$$

which is $2\sqrt{7}$

So $\sqrt{28}$ is $2\sqrt{7}$.

EXAMPLE 13   Simplify $\sqrt{48}$.

$$\sqrt{48} = \sqrt{2 \cdot 2 \cdot 2 \cdot 2 \cdot 3}$$

which is $2 \cdot 2\sqrt{3}$ or $4\sqrt{3}$

So $\sqrt{48}$ is $4\sqrt{3}$.

Sometimes we can see shortcuts and don't have to split into primes. Let's look at $\sqrt{48}$ again.

$$\sqrt{48} \text{ is } \sqrt{16 \cdot 3}$$

But 16 is a perfect square. So $\sqrt{48}$ is $\sqrt{4 \cdot 4 \cdot 3}$ or $4\sqrt{3}$.

EXAMPLE 14   Simplify $-\sqrt{20}$.

$$-\sqrt{20} = -\sqrt{2 \cdot 2 \cdot 5}$$

which is $-2\sqrt{5}$

So $-\sqrt{20}$ is $-2\sqrt{5}$.

EXAMPLE 15   Simplify $3\sqrt{50}$.

$$3\sqrt{50} = 3\sqrt{5 \cdot 5 \cdot 2}$$

which is $3 \cdot 5\sqrt{2}$ or $15\sqrt{2}$

So $3\sqrt{50}$ is $15\sqrt{2}$.

EXAMPLE 16   Simplify $-5\sqrt{12}$.

$$-5\sqrt{12} = -5\sqrt{2 \cdot 2 \cdot 3}$$

which is $-5 \cdot 2\sqrt{3}$ or $-10\sqrt{3}$

So $-5\sqrt{12}$ is $-10\sqrt{3}$.

EXAMPLE 17   Simplify $\dfrac{-7 + \sqrt{16}}{2}$.

$$\frac{-7 + \sqrt{16}}{2} = \frac{-7 + 4}{2} \quad \text{or} \quad -\frac{3}{2}$$

EXAMPLE 18   Simplify $\dfrac{4 - \sqrt{20}}{2}$.

$$\frac{4 - \sqrt{20}}{2} = \frac{4 - \sqrt{2 \cdot 2 \cdot 5}}{2} \quad \text{or} \quad \frac{4 - 2\sqrt{5}}{2}$$

We can simplify this expression by factoring the top and then canceling.

$$\frac{4 - 2\sqrt{5}}{2} = \frac{\overset{1}{\cancel{2}}(2 - \sqrt{5})}{\underset{1}{\cancel{2}}} \quad \text{or} \quad 2 - \sqrt{5}$$

Exercises

Complete the following table and classify each number listed.

Number	Natural	Integer	Rational	Irrational
1. 5				
2. -3				
3. $\sqrt{7}$				
4. $\dfrac{4}{3}$				
5. $2\dfrac{1}{2}$				
6. $\dfrac{7}{-9}$				
7. 0				
8. $3(4+1)$				
9. $\sqrt{17}$				
10. $\sqrt{9}$				
11. $(5)^2$				
12. $-\sqrt{25}$				
13. $3+\sqrt{4}$				
14. $3-\sqrt{5}$				
15. 172				

Split each of the following numbers into its primes.
16.   6
17.   20
18.   25
19.   24
20.   50
21.   75
22.   8
23.   11

Simplify each of the following.
24. 6^2
25. 7^2
26. $(-6)^2$

27. $(-7)^2$

28. $\left(\dfrac{2}{3}\right)^2$

29. $\left(\dfrac{5}{2}\right)^2$

30. $\left(\dfrac{-1}{4}\right)^2$

31. $\left(\dfrac{3}{10}\right)^2$

32. $\sqrt{4}$

33. $\sqrt{25}$

34. $\sqrt{64}$

35. $\sqrt{0}$

36. $\sqrt{\dfrac{9}{4}}$

37. $\sqrt{\dfrac{16}{25}}$

38. $\sqrt{\dfrac{1}{25}}$

39. $\sqrt{\dfrac{9}{16}}$

40. $-\sqrt{49}$

41. $-\sqrt{100}$

42. $(\sqrt{2})^2$

43. $\sqrt{5}\cdot\sqrt{5}$

44. $(\sqrt{7})^2$

45. $\sqrt{0.36}$

46. $\sqrt{0.81}$

47. $\sqrt{5\cdot5}$

48. $\sqrt{0.04}$

49. $\sqrt{10}\,\sqrt{10}$

50. $\sqrt{8}$

51. $\sqrt{12}$

52. $\sqrt{20}$

53. $\sqrt{32}$

54. $\sqrt{50}$

55. $\sqrt{24}$

56. $\sqrt{36}$

57. $\sqrt{99}$

58. $\sqrt{28}$

59. $\sqrt{300}$

60. $2\sqrt{9}$

61. $3\sqrt{8}$

62. $2 + \sqrt{16}$

63. $5 - \sqrt{4}$

64. $2 - 3\sqrt{25}$

65. $4 + 3\sqrt{2}$

66. $-7\sqrt{16}$

67. $-1 - \sqrt{25}$

68. $\dfrac{-5 + \sqrt{36}}{2}$

69. $\dfrac{-4 - \sqrt{49}}{9}$

70. $\dfrac{15 + \sqrt{75}}{5}$

71. $\dfrac{6 - \sqrt{24}}{2}$

Answers to Exercises

number	natural	Integer	Rational	Irrational
① 5	✓	✓	✓	
② −3		✓	✓	
③ $\sqrt{7}$				✓
④ $\frac{4}{3}$			✓	
⑤ $2\frac{1}{2}$			✓	
⑥ $\frac{7}{-9}$			✓	
⑦ 0		✓	✓	
⑧ 3(4+1)	✓	✓	✓	
⑨ $\sqrt{17}$				✓
⑩ $\sqrt{9}$	✓	✓	✓	
⑪ $(5)^2$	✓	✓	✓	
⑫ $-\sqrt{25}$		✓	✓	
⑬ $3+\sqrt{4}$	✓	✓	✓	
⑭ $3-\sqrt{5}$				✓
⑮ 172	✓	✓	✓	

⑯ 6 is 3·2

⑰ 20 is 2·2·5 or $2^2·5$

(18.) 25 is 5·5 or 5^2

(19.) 24 is 2·2·2·3 or $2^3·3$

(20.) 50 is 2·5·5 or $2·5^2$

(21.) 75 is 3·5·5 or $3·5^2$

(22.) 8 is 2·2·2 or 2^3

(23.) 11 is prime

(24.) $6^2 = 36$

(25.) $7^2 = 49$

(26.) $(-6)^2 = 36$

(27.) $(-7)^2 = 49$

(28.) $\left(\frac{2}{3}\right)^2 = \frac{4}{9}$

(29.) $\left(\frac{5}{2}\right)^2 = \frac{25}{4}$

(30.) $\left(-\frac{1}{4}\right)^2 = \frac{1}{16}$

(31.) $\left(\frac{3}{10}\right)^2 = \frac{9}{100}$

(32.) $\sqrt{4} = 2$

(33.) $\sqrt{25} = 5$

(34.) $\sqrt{64} = 8$

(35.) $\sqrt{0} = 0$

(36.) $\sqrt{\frac{9}{4}} = \frac{3}{2}$

(37.) $\sqrt{\frac{16}{25}} = \frac{4}{5}$

(38.) $\sqrt{\frac{1}{25}} = \frac{1}{5}$

(39.) $\sqrt{\frac{9}{16}} = \frac{3}{4}$

(40.) $-\sqrt{49} = -7$

41. $-\sqrt{100} = -10$

42. $(\sqrt{2})^2 = 2$

43. $\sqrt{5} \cdot \sqrt{5} = 5$

44. $(\sqrt{7})^2 = 7$

45. $\sqrt{0.36} = 0.6$

46. $\sqrt{0.81} = 0.9$

47. $\sqrt{5 \cdot 5} = 5$

48. $\sqrt{0.04} = 0.2$

49. $\sqrt{10} \cdot \sqrt{10} = 10$

50. $\sqrt{8} = \sqrt{2 \cdot 2 \cdot 2}$ which is $2\sqrt{2}$

51. $\sqrt{12} = \sqrt{2 \cdot 2 \cdot 3}$ which is $2\sqrt{3}$

52. $\sqrt{20} = \sqrt{2 \cdot 2 \cdot 5}$ which is $2\sqrt{5}$

53. $\sqrt{32} = \sqrt{2 \cdot 2 \cdot 2 \cdot 2 \cdot 2}$ which is $4\sqrt{2}$

54. $\sqrt{50} = \sqrt{2 \cdot 5 \cdot 5}$ which is $5\sqrt{2}$

55. $\sqrt{24} = \sqrt{2 \cdot 2 \cdot 6}$ which is $2\sqrt{6}$

56. $\sqrt{36} = 6$

57. $\sqrt{99} = \sqrt{3 \cdot 3 \cdot 11}$ which is $3\sqrt{11}$

58. $\sqrt{28} = \sqrt{2 \cdot 2 \cdot 7}$ which is $2\sqrt{7}$

59. $\sqrt{300} = \sqrt{3 \cdot 10 \cdot 10}$ which is $10\sqrt{3}$

60. $2\sqrt{9} = 2 \cdot 3$ which is 6

61. $3\sqrt{8} = 3\sqrt{2 \cdot 2 \cdot 2}$ which is $3 \cdot 2\sqrt{2}$ or $6\sqrt{2}$

62. $2 + \sqrt{16} = 2 + 4$ which is 6

63. $5 - \sqrt{4} = 5 - 2$ which is 3

64. $2 - 3\sqrt{25} = 2 - 3 \cdot 5$ or $2 - 15$ which is -13

65. $4 + 3\sqrt{2}$ cannot be simplified

66. $-7\sqrt{16} = -7 \cdot 4$ or -28

67. $-1 - \sqrt{25} = -1 - 5$ or -6

68. $\dfrac{-5 + \sqrt{36}}{2} = \dfrac{-5 + 6}{2}$ or $\dfrac{1}{2}$

69. $\dfrac{-4 - \sqrt{49}}{9} = \dfrac{-4 - 7}{9}$ or $-\dfrac{11}{9}$

70. $\dfrac{15 + \sqrt{75}}{5} = \dfrac{15 + \sqrt{5 \cdot 5 \cdot 3}}{5}$ which is $\dfrac{15 + 5\sqrt{3}}{5}$

    or $3 + \sqrt{3}$

71. $\dfrac{6 - \sqrt{24}}{2} = \dfrac{6 - \sqrt{2 \cdot 2 \cdot 6}}{2}$ which is $\dfrac{6 - 2\sqrt{6}}{2}$

    or $3 - \sqrt{6}$

Additional Exercises

Complete the following table and classify each number listed.

Number	Natural	Integer	Rational	Irrational
1. 6				
2. −2				
3. $\sqrt{5}$				
4. $\dfrac{5}{6}$				
5. $\sqrt{2}$				
6. 10				
7. −8				
8. $\sqrt{3}$				
9. $\sqrt{4}$				
10. $2(4 − 1)$				
11. $\dfrac{-2}{5}$				
12. 4^2				
13. $-\sqrt{16}$				
14. $4 + \sqrt{25}$				
15. $2 + \sqrt{5}$				

Split each of the following numbers into its primes.
16. 9
17. 10
18. 15
19. 48
20. 36
21. 45
22. 16
23. 5

Simplify each of the following.
24. 3^2
25. 8^2
26. $(-3)^2$
27. $(-8)^2$
28. $\left(\dfrac{3}{4}\right)^2$
29. $\left(\dfrac{2}{5}\right)^2$

30. $-\left(\dfrac{1}{3}\right)^2$.

31. $(10)^2$

32. $\sqrt{9}$

33. $\sqrt{36}$

34. $\sqrt{81}$

35. $\sqrt{\dfrac{25}{36}}$

36. $\sqrt{\dfrac{100}{9}}$

37. $\sqrt{\dfrac{1}{36}}$

38. $\sqrt{\dfrac{9}{25}}$

39. $\sqrt{\dfrac{49}{36}}$

40. $-\sqrt{25}$

41. $-\sqrt{4}$

42. $\sqrt{0.64}$

43. $\sqrt{0.49}$

44. $(\sqrt{13})^2$

45. $(\sqrt{341})^2$

46. $\sqrt{0.09}$

47. $\sqrt{7\cdot7}$

48. $\sqrt{\dfrac{9}{49}}$

49. $\sqrt{14\cdot14}$

50. $\sqrt{18}$

51. $\sqrt{27}$

52. $\sqrt{72}$

53. $\sqrt{45}$

54. $\sqrt{75}$

55. $\sqrt{200}$

56. $\sqrt{44}$

57. $\sqrt{28}$

58. $\sqrt{16}$

59. $\sqrt{48}$

60. $3\sqrt{4}$

61. $5\sqrt{16}$

62. $3 + \sqrt{25}$

63. $6 - \sqrt{9}$

64. $-5 - 2\sqrt{9}$

65. $6 + 4\sqrt{3}$

66. $-5\sqrt{36}$

67. $-2 - \sqrt{100}$

68. $\dfrac{-8 + \sqrt{81}}{3}$

69. $\dfrac{3 - \sqrt{36}}{6}$

70. $\dfrac{12 + \sqrt{48}}{4}$

71. $\dfrac{9 - \sqrt{72}}{3}$

Lesson 2

Quadratic Equations

In this lesson, we will solve equations that contain terms like x^2. These equations are called **quadratic equations**.

An equation is a sentence which says that two things are equal. The sentence $x^2 = 9$ is an equation. As it stands, it is not true and it is not false. If we put 3 in place of x, we get $(3)(3) = 9$, which is true. So 3 is a solution of $x^2 = 9$. If we put -3 in place of x, we get $(-3)(-3) = 9$, which is also true. So -3 is <u>also</u> a solution of $x^2 = 9$. Finding the numbers that make an equation true is called **solving** the equation.

EXAMPLE 1 Solve $x^2 = 25$.

To solve this equation we must find a number that we can multiply by itself to get 25.

> 5 works since $(5)(5) = 25$
> -5 also works since $(-5)(-5) = 25$

Note: This equation has two solutions, 5 and -5. Quadratic equations often have two different solutions.

20

EXAMPLE 2   Solve $x^2 = 1$.

We must find a number that we can multiply by itself to get 1.

> 1 works since $(1)(1) = 1$
> -1 also works since $(-1)(-1) = 1$

So the equation $x^2 = 1$ has two solutions, 1 and -1.

EXAMPLE 3   Solve $x^2 = 0$.

We must find a number that we can multiply by itself to get 0.
0 works, since $0 \cdot 0 = 0$. And 0 is the only number that works, so $x^2 = 0$
is a quadratic equation with only one solution.

EXAMPLE 4   Solve $x^2 = 5$.

We must find a number that we can multiply by itself to get 5.

> $\sqrt{5}$ works since $\sqrt{5} \cdot \sqrt{5} = 5$
> $-\sqrt{5}$ works since $(-\sqrt{5})(-\sqrt{5}) = 5$

So the equation $x^2 = 5$ has two solutions, $\sqrt{5}$ and $-\sqrt{5}$.

Sometimes it is difficult to see what numbers make a quadratic equation
true, but there are things we can do that can help. First, notice that zero is
a very special number. That is, if we multiply two numbers and get zero,
then at least one of the numbers must be zero. So the only way the equation
$ab = 0$ can be true is if a is 0 or b is 0. 0 is the only number that has this
property. We will use this to help solve quadratic equations.

EXAMPLE 5   Solve $x^2 - 3x = 0$.

We want to use the fact that when two numbers multiply and give
zero, at least one of the numbers must be zero. So let's factor the left
side and get

$$x(x - 3) = 0$$

This means that x times $(x - 3)$ is 0. There are two ways this can be
true:

$$x = 0 \qquad\qquad \text{or} \qquad\qquad \begin{aligned} x - 3 &= \quad 0 \\ +\,3 &\quad\ \ +3 \\ \hline x &= \quad 3 \end{aligned}$$

So 0 is a solution.   So 3 is a solution.

Let's check each solution.

Put 0 in for x.   Put 3 in for x.

$$\begin{aligned} x^2 - 3x &= 0 \\ 0^2 - 3(0) &= 0 \\ 0 - 0 &= 0 \\ \text{True} \end{aligned} \qquad\qquad \begin{aligned} x^2 - 3x &= 0 \\ (3)^2 - 3(3) &= 0 \\ 9 - 9 &= 0 \\ \text{True} \end{aligned}$$

So the solutions of $x^2 - 3x = 0$ are 0 and 3.

EXAMPLE 6   Solve $x^2 + 4x + 3 = 0$.

Since the right side is 0, we factor the left side.

$$(x + 1)(x + 3) = 0$$

This means that $(x + 1)$ times $(x + 3)$ is 0. There are two ways this can be true:

$$\begin{aligned} x + 1 &= \quad 0 \\ -\,1 &\quad\ \ -1 \\ \hline x &= -1 \end{aligned} \qquad\qquad \text{or} \qquad\qquad \begin{aligned} x + 3 &= \quad 0 \\ -\,3 &\quad\ \ -3 \\ \hline x &= -3 \end{aligned}$$

So -1 is a solution.   So -3 is a solution.

Let's check each solution.

Put -1 in for x.   Put -3 in for x.

$$\begin{aligned} x^2 + 4x + 3 &= 0 \\ (-1)^2 + 4(-1) + 3 &= 0 \\ 1 - 4 + 3 &= 0 \\ 0 &= 0 \\ \text{True} \end{aligned} \qquad \begin{aligned} x^2 + 4x + 3 &= 0 \\ (-3)^2 + 4(-3) + 3 &= 0 \\ 9 - 12 + 3 &= 0 \\ 0 &= 0 \\ \text{True} \end{aligned}$$

So the solutions of $x^2 + 4x + 3 = 0$ are -1 and -3.

EXAMPLE 7 Solve $x^2 - 16 = 0$.

Since the right side is 0, we factor the other side.

$(x + 4)(x - 4) = 0$

This means that $(x + 4)$ times $(x - 4)$ is 0. There are two ways this can be true:

$$
\begin{array}{cc}
x + 4 = & 0 \\
-4 & -4 \\
\hline
x & = -4
\end{array}
\qquad \text{or} \qquad
\begin{array}{cc}
x - 4 = & 0 \\
+4 & +4 \\
\hline
x & = +4
\end{array}
$$

So -4 is a solution. $\qquad$ So $+4$ is a solution.

Let's check each solution.

Put -4 in for x. $\qquad$ Put $+4$ in for x.

$$
\begin{array}{c}
x^2 - 16 = 0 \\
(-4)^2 - 16 = 0 \\
16 - 16 = 0 \\
0 = 0 \\
\underline{\text{True}}
\end{array}
\qquad\qquad
\begin{array}{c}
x^2 - 16 = 0 \\
(4)^2 - 16 = 0 \\
16 - 16 = 0 \\
0 = 0 \\
\underline{\text{True}}
\end{array}
$$

So the solutions of $x^2 - 16 = 0$ are $+4$ and -4.

EXAMPLE 8 Solve $2x^2 + x - 6 = 0$.

Since one side is 0, we factor the other side.

$(2x - 3)(x + 2) = 0$

This means that $(2x - 3)$ times $(x + 2)$ is 0. There are two ways this can be true:

$$2x - 3 = \quad 0 \qquad \text{or} \qquad x + 2 = \quad 0$$
$$\underline{\quad + 3 = +3} \qquad\qquad\qquad \underline{\quad - 2 \quad -2}$$
$$2x \quad = \quad 3 \qquad\qquad\qquad x \quad\quad = -2$$
$$\frac{2x}{2} \quad = \quad \frac{3}{2}$$
$$x = \frac{3}{2}$$

So $\frac{3}{2}$ is a solution.   So -2 is a solution.

Let's check each solution.

Put $\frac{3}{2}$ in for x.   Put -2 in for x.

$$2x^2 + x - 6 = 0 \qquad\qquad\qquad 2x^2 + x - 6 = 0$$
$$2\left(\frac{3}{2}\right)^2 + \frac{3}{2} - 6 = 0 \qquad\qquad 2(-2)^2 + (-2) - 6 = 0$$
$$2\left(\frac{9}{4}\right) + \frac{3}{2} - 6 = 0 \qquad\qquad 2(4) - 2 - 6 = 0$$
$$\frac{9}{2} + \frac{3}{2} - \frac{12}{2} = 0 \qquad\qquad\qquad 8 - 8 = 0$$
$$0 = 0 \qquad\qquad\qquad\qquad 0 = 0$$
$$\underline{\text{True}} \qquad\qquad\qquad\qquad \underline{\text{True}}$$

So the solutions of $2x^2 + x - 6 = 0$ are $\frac{3}{2}$ and -2.

EXAMPLE 9   Solve $x^2 - 6x + 9 = 0$.

Since one side is 0, we factor the other side.

$$(x - 3)(x - 3) = 0$$

This means that $(x - 3)$ times $(x - 3)$ is 0. There is only one way this can be true.

$$x - 3 = \quad 0$$
$$\underline{\quad + 3 \quad +3}$$
$$x \quad\quad = +3$$

So +3 is a solution. Let's check this solution. Put +3 in for x.

$$x^2 - 6x + 9 = 0$$
$$(3)^2 - 6(3) + 9 = 0$$
$$9 - 18 + 9 = 0$$
$$0 = 0 \qquad \text{True}$$

So the solution of $x^2 - 6x + 9 = 0$ is 3.

EXAMPLE 10   Solve $x^2 - 2x = 15$.

Neither side is 0; but one side must be 0 to use the method of previous examples. Let's change the form of the equation.

$$
\begin{array}{rr}
x^2 - 2x = & 15 \\
- 15 & -15 \\
\hline
x^2 - 2x - 15 = & 0
\end{array}
$$

Since one side is now 0, we can factor the other side.

$$(x - 5)(x + 3) = 0$$

This means that $(x - 5)$ times $(x + 3)$ is 0. There are two ways this can be true:

$$
\begin{array}{rr}
x - 5 = & 0 \\
+ 5 & +5 \\
\hline
x \quad = & 5
\end{array}
\qquad \text{or} \qquad
\begin{array}{rr}
x + 3 = & 0 \\
- 3 & -3 \\
\hline
x \quad = & -3
\end{array}
$$

So 5 is the solution. | So −3 is a solution.

Let's check each solution.

Put 5 in for x. | Put −3 in for x.

$$x^2 - 2x = 15$$
$$(5)^2 - 2(5) = 15$$
$$25 - 10 = 15$$
$$15 = 15$$
$$\text{True}$$

$$x^2 - 2x = 15$$
$$(-3)^2 - 2(-3) = 15$$
$$9 + 6 = 15$$
$$15 = 15$$
$$\text{True}$$

So the solutions of $x^2 - 2x = 15$ are 5 and −3.

EXAMPLE 11   Solve $x^2 = 5x$.

Neither side is 0; but one side must be 0 to use the method of previous examples. Let's change the form of the equation.

$$\begin{array}{rr} x^2 = & 5x \\ -5x & -5x \\ \hline x^2 - 5x = & 0 \end{array}$$

Since one side is now 0, we can factor the other side.

$$x(x - 5) = 0$$

This means that x times $(x - 5)$ is 0. There are two ways this can be true:

$$x = 0 \qquad\qquad \text{or} \qquad\qquad \begin{array}{rr} x - 5 = & 0 \\ +5 & +5 \\ \hline x & = +5 \end{array}$$

So 0 is a solution.   So 5 is a solution.

Let's check each solution.

Put 0 in for x.   Put 5 in for x.

$$\begin{array}{l} x^2 = 5x \\ 0^2 = 5(0) \\ \quad 0 = 0 \qquad \underline{\text{True}} \end{array} \qquad\qquad \begin{array}{l} x^2 = 5x \\ 5^2 = 5(5) \\ 25 = 25 \qquad \underline{\text{True}} \end{array}$$

So the solutions of $x^2 = 5x$ are 0 and 5.

EXAMPLE 12 Solve $0 = 3x^2 - 3$.

Since one side is 0, we factor the other side. First we factor out the common monomial factor.

$0 = 3(x^2 - 1)$

We can factor further.

$0 = 3(x - 1)(x + 1)$

This means that 3 times $(x - 1)$ times $(x + 1)$ is 0. Since 3 cannot be 0, there are two ways that $0 = 3(x - 1)(x + 1)$ can be true:

$$0 = x - 1 \qquad\qquad \text{or} \qquad\qquad 0 = x + 1$$
$$\underline{+1 \quad +1} \qquad\qquad\qquad\qquad\qquad \underline{-1 \quad -1}$$
$$+1 = x \qquad\qquad\qquad\qquad\qquad\qquad -1 = x$$

So 1 is a solution. | So -1 is a solution.

Let's check each solution.

Put 1 in for x. | Put -1 in for x.

$0 = 3x^2 - 3$ $0 = 3x^2 - 3$

$0 = 3(1)^2 - 3$ $0 = 3(-1)^2 - 3$

$0 = 3 - 3$ $0 = 3(1) - 3$

$0 = 0$ <u>True</u> $0 = 0$ <u>True</u>

So the solutions of $0 = 3x^2 - 3$ are 1 and -1.

Exercises

Find all solutions of each of the following equations and check each solution.

1. $x^2 = 9$
2. $x^2 = 4$
3. $x^2 - 100 = 0$
4. $x(x - 2) = 0$
5. $x(x + 5) = 0$
6. $2x(x - 4) = 0$
7. $(x + 2)(x + 5) = 0$
8. $(2x - 3)(x + 4) = 0$
9. $x^2 - 5x + 6 = 0$
10. $2x^2 + 10x + 12 = 0$
11. $x^2 - 4 = 0$
12. $x^2 - 4x - 5 = 0$
13. $x^2 + 2x - 8 = 0$
14. $3x^2 - 16x + 5 = 0$
15. $x^2 - 8x + 16 = 0$
16. $x^2 - 64 = 0$
17. $x^2 = -6x$
18. $5x^2 = 5$
19. $x^2 + 10 = 7x$
20. $x^2 + 2x = 3$

Answers to Exercises

(1.) $x^2 = 9$

$(3)(3) = 9$ $(-3)(-3) = 9$

solutions are 3 and −3

(2.) $x^2 = 4$

$(2)(2) = 4$ $(-2)(-2) = 4$

solutions are 2 and −2

(3.) $x^2 - 100 = 0$

$(x + 10)(x - 10) = 0$

$x + 10 = 0$ $x - 10 = 0$

$x = -10$ $x = 10$

solutions are −10 and 10

(4.) $x(x - 2) = 0$

$x = 0$ $x - 2 = 0$

$x = 2$

solutions are 0 and 2

(5.) $x(x + 5) = 0$

$x = 0$ $x + 5 = 0$

$x = -5$

solutions are 0 and −5

(6.) $2x(x - 4) = 0$

$2x = 0$ $x - 4 = 0$

$x = 0$ $x = 4$

solutions are 0 and 4

7. $(x+2)(x+5) = 0$

$x+2 = 0 \qquad x+5 = 0$

$x = -2 \qquad\qquad x = -5$

solutions are -2 and -5

8. $(2x-3)(x+4) = 0$

$2x-3 = 0 \qquad x+4 = 0$

$2x = 3 \qquad\qquad x = -4$

$x = \dfrac{3}{2}$

solutions are $\dfrac{3}{2}$ and -4

9. $x^2 - 5x + 6 = 0$

$(x-3)(x-2) = 0$

$x-3 = 0 \qquad x-2 = 0$

$x = 3 \qquad\qquad x = 2$

solutions are 3 and 2

10. $2x^2 + 10x + 12 = 0$

$2(x^2 + 5x + 6) = 0$

$2(x+3)(x+2) = 0$

$x+3 = 0 \qquad x+2 = 0$

$x = -3 \qquad\qquad x = -2$

solutions are -3 and -2

11. $x^2 - 4 = 0$

$(x+2)(x-2) = 0$

$x+2 = 0 \qquad x-2 = 0$

$x = -2 \qquad\qquad x = 2$

solutions are -2 and 2

12) $x^2 - 4x - 5 = 0$
$(x-5)(x+1) = 0$
$x - 5 = 0 \qquad x + 1 = 0$
$x = 5 \qquad x = -1$
solutions are 5 and -1

13. $x^2 + 2x - 8 = 0$
$(x+4)(x-2) = 0$
$x + 4 = 0 \qquad x - 2 = 0$
$x = -4 \qquad x = 2$
solutions are -4 and 2

14.) $3x^2 - 16x + 5 = 0$
$(3x - 1)(x - 5) = 0$
$3x - 1 = 0 \qquad x - 5 = 0$
$3x = 1 \qquad x = 5$
$x = \frac{1}{3}$
solutions are $\frac{1}{3}$ and 5

15.) $x^2 - 8x + 16 = 0$
$(x-4)(x-4) = 0$
$x - 4 = 0$
$x = 4 \qquad\qquad$ solution is 4

16.) $x^2 - 64 = 0$
$(x+8)(x-8) = 0 \qquad x - 8 = 0$
$x + 8 = 0 \qquad\qquad x = 8$
$x = -8$
solutions are -8 and 8

(17.) $x^2 = -6x$

$x^2 + 6x = 0$

$x(x+6) = 0$ $x+6 = 0$

$x = 0$ $x = -6$

solutions are 0 and -6

(18.) $5x^2 = 5$

$5x^2 - 5 = 0$

$5(x^2 - 1) = 0$

$5(x+1)(x-1) = 0$

$x+1 = 0$ $x-1 = 0$

$x = -1$ $x = 1$

solutions are -1 and 1

(19.) $x^2 + 10 = 7x$

$x^2 - 7x + 10 = 0$

$(x-2)(x-5) = 0$

$x-2 = 0$ $x-5 = 0$

$x = 2$ $x = 5$

solutions are 2 and 5

(20.) $x^2 + 2x = 3$

$x^2 + 2x - 3 = 0$

$(x+3)(x-1) = 0$

$x+3 = 0$ $x-1 = 0$

$x = -3$ $x = 1$

solutions are -3 and 1

Additional Exercises

Find all solutions of each of the following equations and check each solution.

1. $x^2 = 25$
2. $x^2 = 16$
3. $x^2 - 49 = 0$
4. $x(x - 3) = 0$
5. $x(x + 8) = 0$
6. $3x(x - 2) = 0$
7. $(x + 3)(x + 7) = 0$
8. $(3x - 5)(x - 1) = 0$
9. $x^2 - 6x + 8 = 0$
10. $3x^2 + 21x + 30 = 0$
11. $x^2 - 81 = 0$
12. $x^2 - 2x - 15 = 0$
13. $x^2 + 8x - 9 = 0$
14. $2x^2 - 15x + 7 = 0$
15. $x^2 - 12x + 36 = 0$
16. $x^2 - 36 = 0$
17. $x^2 = -8x$
18. $12x^2 = 12$
19. $x^2 + 4x = 12$
20. $x^2 + 14 = 9x$

The Quadratic Formulas

There are some quadratic equations that are difficult to factor, and others that are impossible to factor. In this lesson we will use formulas to solve any quadratic equation.

Every quadratic equation can be written in the following standard form.

$$ax^2 + bx + c = 0$$

where a, b, and c stand for numbers, and a cannot be zero. In examples 1 through 7 we find a, b, and c when each of the equations is in the form $ax^2 + bx + c = 0$.

EXAMPLE 1 Find a, b, and c for $2x^2 + 7x + 4 = 0$.

$$ax^2 + bx + c = 0$$
$$2x^2 + 7x + 4 = 0$$

So $a = 2$, $b = 7$, and $c = 4$.

EXAMPLE 2   Find a, b, and c for $x^2 + 5x + 3 = 0$.

Note: $x^2 = 1x^2$.

$$ax^2 + bx + c = 0$$
$$1x^2 + 5x + 3 = 0$$

So $a = 1$, $b = 5$, and $c = 3$.

EXAMPLE 3   Find a, b, and c for $x^2 - 7x + 4 = 0$.

$$ax^2 + bx + c = 0$$
$$1x^2 - 7x + 4 = 0$$

So $a = 1$, $b = -7$, and $c = 4$.

EXAMPLE 4   Find a, b, and c for $x^2 - 10x - 1 = 0$.

$$ax^2 + bx + c = 0$$
$$1x^2 - 10x - 1 = 0$$

So $a = 1$, $b = -10$, and $c = -1$.

EXAMPLE 5   Find a, b, and c for $x^2 + 3x = 0$.

Note: We put 0 in for the missing term.

$$ax^2 + bx + c = 0$$
$$1x^2 + 3x + 0 = 0$$

So $a = 1$, $b = 3$, and $c = 0$.

EXAMPLE 6   Find a, b, and c for $3x^2 - 4 = 0$.

Note: We put in $0x$ (which is 0) for the missing term.

$$ax^2 + bx + c = 0$$
$$3x^2 + 0x - 4 = 0$$

So $a = 3$, $b = 0$, and $c = -4$.

EXAMPLE 7   Find a, b, and c for $x^2 = 4 - x$.

This equation is not in standard form, so let's change it to the form $ax^2 + bx + c = 0$.

$$
\begin{array}{rcr}
x^2 & = & 4 - x \\
\text{add } +x \quad\quad + x & & + x \\
\hline
x^2 + x & = & 4 \\
\text{add } -4 \quad\quad - 4 & & -4 \\
\hline
x^2 + x - 4 & = & 0
\end{array}
$$

$$
\begin{array}{c}
ax^2 + bx + c = 0 \\
\downarrow \quad\quad \downarrow \quad\quad \downarrow \\
1x^2 + 1x - 4 = 0
\end{array}
$$

So $a = 1$, $b = 1$, and $c = -4$.

When a quadratic equation is in standard form, $ax^2 + bx + c = 0$, we can use the following two formulas to find the solutions.

$$
x = \frac{-b + \sqrt{b^2 - 4ac}}{2a}
$$

$$
x = \frac{-b - \sqrt{b^2 - 4ac}}{2a}
$$

Note: There are two formulas because most quadratic equations have two different solutions.

EXAMPLE 8   Solve $x^2 + 4x + 3 = 0$ using the quadratic formulas.

In Lesson 2, example 6, we found the solutions -1 and -3 by factoring. Now we will use the quadratic formulas and get the same solutions. This equation is in standard form:

$$
\begin{array}{c}
ax^2 + bx + c = 0 \\
\downarrow \quad\quad \downarrow \quad\quad \downarrow \\
1x^2 + 4x + 3 = 0
\end{array}
$$

So $a = 1$, $b = 4$, and $c = 3$. In each quadratic formula we put in 1 for a, 4 for b, and 3 for c.

$$x = \frac{-b + \sqrt{b^2 - 4ac}}{2a} \qquad\qquad x = \frac{-b - \sqrt{b^2 - 4ac}}{2a}$$

$$x = \frac{-4 + \sqrt{(4)^2 - 4(1)(3)}}{2(1)} \qquad\qquad x = \frac{-4 - \sqrt{(4)^2 - 4(1)(3)}}{2(1)}$$

$$x = \frac{-4 + \sqrt{16 - 12}}{2} \qquad\qquad x = \frac{-4 - \sqrt{16 - 12}}{2}$$

$$x = \frac{-4 + \sqrt{4}}{2} \qquad\qquad x = \frac{-4 - \sqrt{4}}{2}$$

$$x = \frac{-4 + 2}{2} \qquad\qquad x = \frac{-4 - 2}{2}$$

$$x = \frac{-2}{2} \qquad\qquad x = \frac{-6}{2}$$

$$x = -1 \qquad\qquad x = -3$$

So the solutions of $x^2 + 4x + 3 = 0$ are -1 and -3, the same solutions we got in Lesson 2 by factoring.

Now let's solve a quadratic equation that cannot be factored.

EXAMPLE 9   Solve $2x^2 + 7x + 4 = 0$ using the quadratic formulas.

This equation is in standard form, so $a = 2$, $b = 7$, and $c = 4$. In each quadratic formula we put in 2 for a, 7 for b, and 4 for c.

$$x = \frac{-b + \sqrt{b^2 - 4ac}}{2a} \qquad\qquad x = \frac{-b - \sqrt{b^2 - 4ac}}{2a}$$

$$x = \frac{-7 + \sqrt{(7)^2 - 4(2)(4)}}{2(2)} \qquad\qquad x = \frac{-7 - \sqrt{(7)^2 - 4(2)(4)}}{2(2)}$$

$$x = \frac{-7 + \sqrt{49 - 32}}{4} \qquad\qquad x = \frac{-7 - \sqrt{49 - 32}}{4}$$

$$x = \frac{-7 + \sqrt{17}}{4} \qquad\qquad x = \frac{-7 - \sqrt{17}}{4}$$

So the solutions of $2x^2 + 7x + 4 = 0$ are $\dfrac{-7 + \sqrt{17}}{4}$ and $\dfrac{-7 - \sqrt{17}}{4}$.

EXAMPLE 10   Solve $x^2 + 5x + 3 = 0$ using the quadratic formulas.

This equation is in standard form, so $a = 1$, $b = 5$, and $c = 3$. Put 1 in for a, 5 for b and 3 for c.

$$x = \frac{-b + \sqrt{b^2 - 4ac}}{2a} \qquad\qquad x = \frac{-b - \sqrt{b^2 - 4ac}}{2a}$$

$$x = \frac{-5 + \sqrt{(5)^2 - 4(1)(3)}}{2(1)} \qquad\qquad x = \frac{-5 - \sqrt{(5)^2 - 4(1)(3)}}{2(1)}$$

$$x = \frac{-5 + \sqrt{25 - 12}}{2} \qquad\qquad x = \frac{-5 - \sqrt{25 - 12}}{2}$$

$$x = \frac{-5 + \sqrt{13}}{2} \qquad\qquad x = \frac{-5 - \sqrt{13}}{2}$$

So the solutions of $x^2 + 5x + 3 = 0$ are $\dfrac{-5 + \sqrt{13}}{2}$ and $\dfrac{-5 - \sqrt{13}}{2}$.

EXAMPLE 11   Solve $x^2 - 7x + 4 = 0$ using the quadratic formulas.

This equation is in standard form, so $a = 1$, $b = -7$, and $c = 4$. Put in 1 for a, -7 for b and 4 for c.

$$x = \frac{-b + \sqrt{b^2 - 4ac}}{2a} \qquad\qquad x = \frac{-b - \sqrt{b^2 - 4ac}}{2a}$$

$$x = \frac{-(-7) + \sqrt{(-7)^2 - 4(1)(4)}}{2(1)} \qquad\qquad x = \frac{-(-7) - \sqrt{(-7)^2 - 4(1)(4)}}{2(1)}$$

$$x = \frac{7 + \sqrt{49 - 16}}{2} \qquad\qquad x = \frac{7 - \sqrt{49 - 16}}{2}$$

$$x = \frac{7 + \sqrt{33}}{2} \qquad\qquad x = \frac{7 - \sqrt{33}}{2}$$

So the solutions of $x^2 - 7x + 4 = 0$ are $\dfrac{7 + \sqrt{33}}{2}$ and $\dfrac{7 - \sqrt{33}}{2}$.

EXAMPLE 12   Solve $x^2 - 4x + 13 = 0$ using the quadratic formulas.

This equation is in standard form, so $a = 1$, $b = -4$, and $c = 13$. Put in 1 for a, -4 for b, and 13 for c.

$$x = \frac{-b + \sqrt{b^2 - 4ac}}{2a} \qquad x = \frac{-b - \sqrt{b^2 - 4ac}}{2a}$$

$$x = \frac{-(-4) + \sqrt{(-4)^2 - 4(1)(13)}}{2(1)} \qquad x = \frac{-(-4) - \sqrt{(-4)^2 - 4(1)(13)}}{2}$$

$$x = \frac{4 + \sqrt{16 - 52}}{2} \qquad x = \frac{4 - \sqrt{16 - 52}}{2}$$

$$x = \frac{4 + \sqrt{-36}}{2} \qquad x = \frac{4 - \sqrt{-36}}{2}$$

Note: Each of the solutions contains the number $\sqrt{-36}$.

$\sqrt{-36}$ is <u>not</u> $+6$ because $(+6)^2 = +36$.

$\sqrt{-36}$ is <u>not</u> -6 because $(-6)^2 = +36$.

$\sqrt{-36}$ cannot be a positive number because when you multiply two positive numbers you get a positive number.

$\sqrt{-36}$ cannot be a negative number because when you multiply two negative numbers you get a positive number.

$\sqrt{-36}$ cannot be 0 since $0^2 = 0$.

Since every real number has to be either positive, negative or zero, $\sqrt{-36}$ is not a real number. So the equation $x^2 - 4x + 13 = 0$ has no solutions which are real numbers.

EXAMPLE 13   Solve $x^2 - 5 = 0$ using the quadratic formulas.

In standard form, this equation is $1x^2 + 0x - 5 = 0$, so $a = 1$, $b = 0$, and $c = -5$. Put in 1 for a, 0 for b, and -5 for c.

$$x = \frac{-b + \sqrt{b^2 - 4ac}}{2a} \qquad\qquad x = \frac{-b - \sqrt{b^2 - 4ac}}{2a}$$

$$x = \frac{-0 + \sqrt{(0)^2 - 4(1)(-5)}}{2(1)} \qquad x = \frac{-0 - \sqrt{(0)^2 - 4(1)(-5)}}{2(1)}$$

$$x = \frac{0 + \sqrt{20}}{2} \qquad\qquad x = \frac{0 - \sqrt{20}}{2}$$

$$x = \frac{\sqrt{20}}{2} \qquad\qquad x = \frac{-\sqrt{20}}{2}$$

We can simplify. We can simplify.

$$x = \frac{\sqrt{2 \cdot 2 \cdot 5}}{2} \qquad\qquad x = -\frac{\sqrt{2 \cdot 2 \cdot 5}}{2}$$

$$x = \frac{2\sqrt{5}}{2} \qquad\qquad x = -\frac{2\sqrt{5}}{2}$$

$$x = \sqrt{5} \qquad\qquad x = -\sqrt{5}$$

So the solutions of $x^2 - 5 = 0$ are $\sqrt{5}$ and $-\sqrt{5}$.

EXAMPLE 14   Solve $x^2 + 1 = 4x$ using the quadratic formulas.

This equation is not in standard form, so we will change its form.

$$
\begin{array}{rcr}
x^2 \qquad + 1 = & & 4x \\
\text{Add } -4x \qquad - 4x & & -4x \\
\hline
x^2 - 4x + 1 = & & 0
\end{array}
$$

Now the equation is in standard form. So $a = 1$, $b = -4$, and $c = 1$.
Put in 1 for a, -4 for b, and 1 for c.

$$x = \frac{-b + \sqrt{b^2 - 4ac}}{2a} \qquad\qquad x = \frac{-b - \sqrt{b^2 - 4ac}}{2a}$$

$$x = \frac{-(-4) + \sqrt{(-4)^2 - 4(1)(1)}}{2(1)} \qquad\qquad x = \frac{-(-4) - \sqrt{(-4)^2 - 4(1)(1)}}{2(1)}$$

$$x = \frac{4 + \sqrt{16 - 4}}{2} \qquad\qquad x = \frac{4 - \sqrt{16 - 4}}{2}$$

$$x = \frac{4 + \sqrt{12}}{2} \qquad\qquad x = \frac{4 - \sqrt{12}}{2}$$

$$x = \frac{4 + \sqrt{2 \cdot 2 \cdot 3}}{2} \qquad\qquad x = \frac{4 - \sqrt{2 \cdot 2 \cdot 3}}{2}$$

$$x = \frac{4 + 2\sqrt{3}}{2} \qquad\qquad x = \frac{4 - 2\sqrt{3}}{2}$$

Now factor the top.   Now factor the top.

$$x = \frac{\overset{1}{\cancel{2}}(2 + \sqrt{3})}{\underset{1}{\cancel{2}}} \qquad\qquad x = \frac{\overset{1}{\cancel{2}}(2 - \sqrt{3})}{\underset{1}{\cancel{2}}}$$

$$x = 2 + \sqrt{3} \qquad\qquad x = 2 - \sqrt{3}$$

So the solutions of $x^2 + 1 = 4x$ are $2 + \sqrt{3}$ and $2 - \sqrt{3}$.

EXAMPLE 15   Solve $-3x^2 + 5x - 2 = 0$ using the quadratic formulas.

This equation is in standard form, so $a = -3$, $b = 5$, and $c = -2$. Put in -3 for a, 5 for b, and -2 for c.

$$x = \frac{-b + \sqrt{b^2 - 4ac}}{2a} \qquad\qquad x = \frac{-b - \sqrt{b^2 - 4ac}}{2a}$$

$$x = \frac{-5 + \sqrt{(5)^2 - 4(-3)(-2)}}{2(-3)} \qquad x = \frac{-5 - \sqrt{(5)^2 - 4(-3)(-2)}}{2(-3)}$$

$$x = \frac{-5 + \sqrt{25 - 24}}{-6} \qquad\qquad x = \frac{-5 - \sqrt{25 - 24}}{-6}$$

$$x = \frac{-5 + \sqrt{1}}{-6} \qquad\qquad x = \frac{-5 - \sqrt{1}}{-6}$$

$$x = \frac{-5 + 1}{-6} \qquad\qquad x = \frac{-5 - 1}{-6}$$

$$x = \frac{-4}{-6} \qquad\qquad x = \frac{-6}{-6}$$

$$x = \frac{2}{3} \qquad\qquad x = 1$$

So the solutions of $-3x^2 + 5x - 2 = 0$ are $\dfrac{2}{3}$ and 1.

Note: Frequently the two quadratic formulas,

$$x = \frac{-b + \sqrt{b^2 - 4ac}}{2a} \quad \text{and} \quad x = \frac{-b - \sqrt{b^2 - 4ac}}{2a},$$

are combined in the following form:

$$x = \frac{-b \pm \sqrt{b^2 - 4ac}}{2a}$$

This form is useful since it saves a lot of writing.

Exercises

Write each of the following equations in the standard form $ax^2 + bx + c = 0$ and find a, b, and c.

1. $2x^2 - 5x + 7 = 0$
2. $x^2 + 4x - 2 = 0$
3. $-x^2 + 3x + 1 = 0$
4. $x^2 + 5x = -6$
5. $x^2 - 4 = 0$
6. $x^2 + 1 = 2x$
7. $-3x^2 + 3 = 0$
8. $2x^2 = 3x$

Solve each of the following equations. Use the quadratic formulas if you cannot factor.

9. $x^2 + x - 12 = 0$
10. $x^2 + 7x + 4 = 0$
11. $x^2 - 5x + 3 = 0$
12. $x^2 + 7x + 2 = 0$
13. $2x^2 + 7x - 3 = 0$
14. $4x^2 + 5x - 3 = 0$
15. $2x^2 - 5x = 8$
16. $2x^2 + 5x + 1 = 0$
17. $-x^2 = 2x - 1$
18. $5 - 8x = x^2$
19. $-x^2 + x + 1 = 0$
20. $x^2 - x = 32$
21. $2x^2 - 5 = 0$
22. $3x^2 = 15$

Answers to Exercises

(1.) $2x^2 - 5x + 7 = 0$
$ax^2 + bx + c = 0$
$a = 2, b = -5, c = 7$

(6.) $x^2 + 1 = 2x$
$x^2 - 2x + 1 = 0$
$a = 1, b = -2, c = 1$

(2.) $x^2 + 4x - 2 = 0$
$ax^2 + bx + c = 0$
$a = 1, b = 4, c = -2$

(7.) $-3x^2 + 3 = 0$
$-3x^2 + 0x + 3 = 0$
$a = -3, b = 0, c = 3$

(3.) $-x^2 + 3x + 1 = 0$
$a = -1, b = 3, c = 1$

(8.) $2x^2 = 3x$
$2x^2 - 3x + 0 = 0$
$a = 2, b = -3, c = 0$

(4.) $x^2 + 5x = -6$
$x^2 + 5x + 6 = 0$
$a = 1, b = 5, c = +6$

(9.) $x^2 + x - 12 = 0$
$(x + 4)(x - 3) = 0$
$x + 4 = 0 \qquad x - 3 = 0$
$x = -4 \qquad x = 3$
solutions are -4 and 3

(5.) $x^2 - 4 = 0$
$x^2 + 0x - 4 = 0$
$a = 1, b = 0, c = -4$

when we write the quadratic formulas,

$x = \dfrac{-b \pm \sqrt{b^2 - 4ac}}{2a}$ stands for two

formulas $x = \dfrac{-b + \sqrt{b^2 - 4ac}}{2a}$

and $x = \dfrac{-b - \sqrt{b^2 - 4ac}}{2a}$

(10.) $x^2 + 7x + 4 = 0$ $a = 1,\ b = 7,\ c = 4$

$x = \dfrac{-b \pm \sqrt{b^2 - 4ac}}{2a}$

$x = \dfrac{-7 \pm \sqrt{7^2 - 4(1)(4)}}{2(1)}$

$x = \dfrac{-7 \pm \sqrt{49 - 16}}{2}$

$x = \dfrac{-7 \pm \sqrt{33}}{2}$

solutions are $\dfrac{-7 + \sqrt{33}}{2}$ and $\dfrac{-7 - \sqrt{33}}{2}$

(11.) $x^2 - 5x + 3 = 0$ $a = 1,\ b = -5,\ c = 3$

$x = \dfrac{-(-5) \pm \sqrt{(-5)^2 - 4(1)(3)}}{2(1)}$

$x = \dfrac{5 \pm \sqrt{25 - 12}}{2}$

$x = \dfrac{5 \pm \sqrt{13}}{2}$

solutions are $\dfrac{5 + \sqrt{13}}{2}$ and $\dfrac{5 - \sqrt{13}}{2}$

(12.) $x^2 + 7x + 2 = 0$ $a = 1,\ b = 7,\ c = 2$

$x = \dfrac{-7 \pm \sqrt{7^2 - 4(1)(2)}}{2(1)}$

$x = \dfrac{-7 \pm \sqrt{49 - 8}}{2}$

$x = \dfrac{-7 \pm \sqrt{41}}{2}$

solutions are $\dfrac{-7 + \sqrt{41}}{2}$ and $\dfrac{-7 - \sqrt{41}}{2}$

(13.) $2x^2 + 7x - 3 = 0$ $a = 2,\ b = 7,\ c = -3$

$x = \dfrac{-7 \pm \sqrt{7^2 - 4(2)(-3)}}{2(2)}$

$x = \dfrac{-7 \pm \sqrt{49 + 24}}{4}$

$x = \dfrac{-7 \pm \sqrt{73}}{4}$

solutions are $\dfrac{-7 + \sqrt{73}}{4}$ and $\dfrac{-7 - \sqrt{73}}{4}$

(14.) $4x^2 + 5x - 3 = 0$ $a = 4,\ b = 5,\ c = -3$

$x = \dfrac{-5 \pm \sqrt{5^2 - 4(4)(-3)}}{2(4)}$

$x = \dfrac{-5 \pm \sqrt{25 + 48}}{8}$

$x = \dfrac{-5 \pm \sqrt{73}}{8}$

solutions are $\dfrac{-5 + \sqrt{73}}{8}$ and $\dfrac{-5 - \sqrt{73}}{8}$

(15.) $2x^2 - 5x = 8$

$2x^2 - 5x - 8 = 0$ $a = 2, b = -5, c = -8$

$x = \dfrac{-(-5) \pm \sqrt{(-5)^2 - 4(2)(-8)}}{2(2)}$

$x = \dfrac{5 \pm \sqrt{25 + 64}}{4}$

$x = \dfrac{5 \pm \sqrt{89}}{4}$

solutions are $\dfrac{5 + \sqrt{89}}{4}$ and $\dfrac{5 - \sqrt{89}}{4}$

(16.) $2x^2 + 5x + 1 = 0$ $a = 2, b = 5, c = 1$

$x = \dfrac{-5 \pm \sqrt{5^2 - 4(2)(1)}}{2(2)}$

$x = \dfrac{-5 \pm \sqrt{25 - 8}}{4}$

$x = \dfrac{-5 \pm \sqrt{17}}{4}$

solutions are $\dfrac{-5 + \sqrt{17}}{4}$ and $\dfrac{-5 - \sqrt{17}}{4}$

(17.) $-x^2 = 2x - 1$

$-x^2 - 2x + 1 = 0$ $a = -1, b = -2, c = 1$

(17.) Continued

$$x = \frac{-(-2) \pm \sqrt{(-2)^2 - 4(-1)(1)}}{2(-1)}$$

$$x = \frac{2 \pm \sqrt{4+4}}{-2}$$

$$x = \frac{2 \pm \sqrt{8}}{-2} \quad \text{or} \quad \frac{2 \pm \sqrt{2 \cdot 2 \cdot 2}}{-2}$$

$$x = \frac{2 \pm 2\sqrt{2}}{-2} \quad \text{or} \quad \frac{2(1 \pm \sqrt{2})}{2(-1)} = -1 \mp \sqrt{2}$$

solutions are $-1 - \sqrt{2}$ and $-1 + \sqrt{2}$

(18.) $5 - 8x = x^2$

$0 = x^2 + 8x - 5$ $a = 1, b = 8, c = -5$

$$x = \frac{-8 \pm \sqrt{8^2 - 4(1)(-5)}}{2(1)}$$
$\left[\begin{array}{l} \text{note: the equation} \\ -x^2 - 8x + 5 = 0 \text{ has} \\ \text{the same solutions} \end{array} \right]$

$$x = \frac{-8 \pm \sqrt{64 + 20}}{2} \quad \text{or} \quad \frac{-8 \pm \sqrt{84}}{2}$$

$$x = \frac{-8 \pm 2\sqrt{21}}{2} \quad \text{or} \quad \frac{2(-4 \pm \sqrt{21})}{2}$$

solutions are $-4 + \sqrt{21}$ and $-4 - \sqrt{21}$

(19.) $-x^2 + x + 1 = 0$ $a = -1, b = 1, c = 1$

$$x = \frac{-1 \pm \sqrt{1^2 - 4(-1)(1)}}{2(-1)}$$

(19) Continued

$$X = \frac{-1 \pm \sqrt{1+4}}{-2}$$

$$X = \frac{-1 \pm \sqrt{5}}{-2}$$

solutions are $\dfrac{-1+\sqrt{5}}{-2}$ and $\dfrac{-1-\sqrt{5}}{-2}$

(20) $X^2 - X = 32$

$X^2 - X - 32 = 0$ $a = 1, b = -1, c = -32$

$$X = \frac{-(-1) \pm \sqrt{(-1)^2 - 4(+1)(-32)}}{2(1)}$$

$$X = \frac{1 \pm \sqrt{1+128}}{2}$$

$$X = \frac{1 \pm \sqrt{129}}{2}$$

solutions are $\dfrac{1+\sqrt{129}}{2}$ and $\dfrac{1-\sqrt{129}}{2}$

(21) $2X^2 - 5 = 0$

$2X^2 + 0X - 5 = 0$ $a = 2, b = 0, C = -5$

$$X = \frac{-0 \pm \sqrt{0^2 - 4(2)(-5)}}{2(2)}$$

(21.) Continued

$$x = \frac{0 \pm \sqrt{0 + 40}}{4}$$

$$x = \frac{\pm \sqrt{40}}{4} \quad or \quad \frac{\pm \sqrt{2 \cdot 2 \cdot 2 \cdot 5}}{4}$$

$$x = \frac{\pm 2\sqrt{10}}{4} \quad or \quad \frac{\pm \cancel{2}\sqrt{10}}{\cancel{2} \cdot 2}$$

solutions are $\frac{\sqrt{10}}{2}$ and $\frac{-\sqrt{10}}{2}$

(22.) $3x^2 = 15$

$3x^2 + 0x - 15 = 0 \qquad a = 3, \ b = 0, \ C = -15$

$$x = \frac{-0 \pm \sqrt{0^2 - 4(3)(-15)}}{2(3)}$$

$$x = \frac{0 \pm \sqrt{4 \cdot 3 \cdot 15}}{6}$$

$$x = \frac{\pm \sqrt{2 \cdot 2 \cdot 3 \cdot 3 \cdot 5}}{6} \quad or \quad \frac{\pm 2 \cdot 3\sqrt{5}}{6}$$

$$x = \frac{\pm \cancel{2} \cdot \cancel{3}\sqrt{5}}{\cancel{2} \cdot \cancel{3}} \quad or \quad \pm\sqrt{5}$$

solutions are $\sqrt{5}$ and $-\sqrt{5}$

Additional Exercises

Write each of the following equations in the standard form $ax^2 + bx + c = 0$ and find a, b and c.

1. $x^2 + 7x + 3 = 0$
2. $3x^2 - 4x + 1 = 0$
3. $-x^2 + 5x + 4 = 0$
4. $x^2 + 6x = 7$
5. $x^2 - 9 = 0$
6. $x^2 + 3 = 5x$
7. $-5x^2 - 5 = 0$
8. $4x^2 = 9x$

Solve each of the following equations. Use the quadratic formulas if you cannot factor.

9. $x^2 + x - 20 = 0$
10. $x^2 + 3x - 3 = 0$
11. $x^2 + 7x + 3 = 0$
12. $3x^2 - 9x + 5 = 0$
13. $4x^2 + 3x - 2 = 0$
14. $5x^2 - 3x = 1$
15. $3x^2 = 5x + 1$
16. $4x^2 - 3x = 5$
17. $-3x^2 + x + 3 = 0$
18. $3x^2 - 2 = 0$
19. $2x - 1 = x^2$
20. $x^2 - x = 25$
21. $7x^2 - 2x - 1 = 0$
22. $25x^2 + 9x - 2 = 0$

Lesson 4

Graphing Quadratics

The sentence $y = x^2 - 5x + 4$ is a quadratic equation with two variables. As it stands, it is not true and it is not false. If we put in a pair of numbers, the equation will become either true or false. Let's try 3 for x and -2 for y.

$$
\begin{aligned}
y &= x^2 - 5x + 4 \\
-2 &= 3^2 - 5(3) + 4 \\
-2 &= 9 - 15 + 4 \\
-2 &= -2 \quad \underline{\text{True!}}
\end{aligned}
$$

So, $(3, -2)$ is a solution of $y = x^2 - 5x + 4$.

In $y = x^2 - 5x + 4$ you must put in two numbers (one for x and one for y) before you can tell if the sentence is true. Finding the pairs of numbers that make this kind of equation true is called **solving** the equation. So one solution of this equation is $(3, -2)$. We always write the numbers in (x, y) order with parentheses; that is, the "x" is the first number, and the "y" is the second number. The first number is called the **x-coordinate** of the solution and the second number is called the **y-coordinate** of the solution.

We can find another solution by picking any number for x and putting it into the equation for each x. This gives us a number for y. This (x, y) pair will make the sentence true. For example, we can find more solutions of $y = x^2 - 5x + 4$ in the following way.

If x is 6, then

$$y = 6^2 - 5(6) + 4$$
$$y = 36 - 30 + 4$$
$$y = 10$$

So $(6, 10)$ is a solution.

If x is 5, then

$$y = (5)^2 - 5(5) + 4$$
$$y = 25 - 25 + 4$$
$$y = 4$$

So $(5, 4)$ is a solution.

One way of keeping track of solutions is to build a table as follows.

x	$x^2 - 5x + 4$	y	Solution
6	$36 - 30 + 4$	10	$(6, 10)$
5	$25 - 25 + 4$	4	$(5, 4)$
4	$16 - 20 + 4$	0	$(4, 0)$
3	$9 - 15 + 4$	-2	$(3, -2)$
2	$4 - 10 + 4$	-2	$(2, -2)$
1	$1 - 5 + 4$	0	$(1, 0)$
0	$0 - 0 + 4$	4	$(0, 4)$
-1	$1 + 5 + 4$	10	$(-1, 10)$

We can plot these solutions on a graph. See Figure 1.

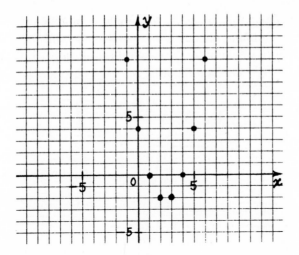

Figure 1

Note: Although these points are not in a straight line, they do form
a pattern. In fact if we plotted all the solutions to the equation
$y = x^2 - 5x + 4$ they would fit into the same pattern. Plotting fractional

solutions such as $\left(\dfrac{3}{2}, -\dfrac{5}{4}\right)$, $\left(\dfrac{9}{2}, \dfrac{7}{4}\right)$, $\left(\dfrac{5}{2}, -\dfrac{9}{4}\right)$ will help fill in the

pattern. See Figure 2.

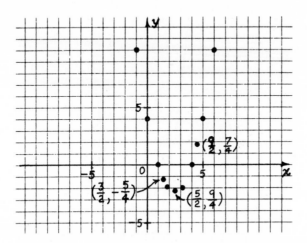

Figure 2

If all the solutions of $y = x^2 - 5x + 4$ could be plotted, the pattern would be completely filled in and would go on forever. But since the paper doesn't go on forever, Figure 3 shows only a small part of the pattern. The pattern for $y = x^2 - 5x + 4$ is called a **parabola**.

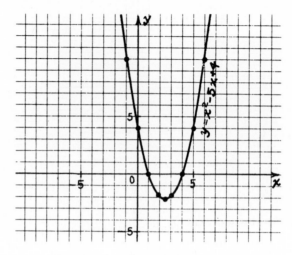

Figure 3

Every point on this parabola is a solution of the equation $y = x^2 - 5x + 4$. For example, the point $(-2, 18)$ is on the parabola. See Figure 4.

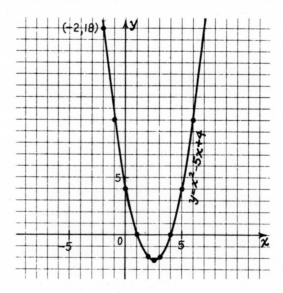

Figure 4

To check that $(-2, 18)$ is really a solution of $y = x^2 - 4x + 4$, put -2 in for x and 18 in for y.

$$y = x^2 - 5x + 4$$
$$18 = (-2)^2 - 5(-2) + 4$$
$$18 = 4 + 10 + 4$$
$$18 = 18 \quad \underline{\text{True!}}$$

So $(-2, 18)$ is a solution of $y = x^2 - 5x + 4$.

Any point <u>not on</u> this parabola <u>is not</u> a solution of the equation. For example, $(3, 4)$ is not on the graph. See Figure 5.

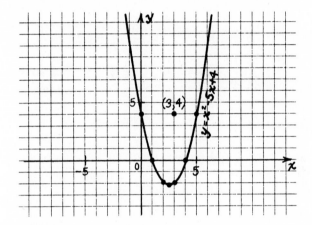

Figure 5

To show that $(3, 4)$ is not a solution of the equation, put 3 in for x and 4 in for y.

$$y = x^2 - 5x + 4$$
$$4 = (3)^2 - 5(3) + 4$$
$$4 = 9 - 15 + 4$$
$$4 = -2 \quad \underline{\text{False}}$$

So $(3, 4)$ is <u>not</u> a solution of $y = x^2 - 5x + 4$.

Every time we graph the solutions of a quadratic equation in the form $y = ax^2 + bx + c$, where a is not zero, the pattern is a parabola. There are parabolas in everyday life. For example, when a ball is thrown into the air, its path is a parabola. See Figure 6.

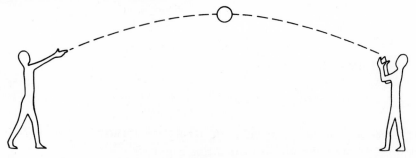

Figure 6

EXAMPLE 1   Graph the solution of $y = x^2 + 2x - 1$.

This is a quadratic equation and its graph is a parabola. Let's graph it. We build a table of solutions using 0, 1, 2, and 3 for x.

x	$x^2 + 2x - 1$	y	Plot (x, y)
0	$0 + 0 - 1$	-1	$(0, -1)$
1	$1 + 2 - 1$	2	$(1, 2)$
2	$4 + 4 - 1$	7	$(2, 7)$
3	$9 + 6 - 1$	14	$(3, 14)$

We plot these solutions in Figure 7.

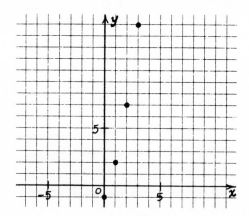

Figure 7

This looks like half a parabola. Let's pick numbers for x that will give us the other half. Putting in -1, -2, -3, and -4 for x will help.

x	$x^2 + 2x - 1$	y	Plot (x, y)
-1	$1 - 2 - 1$	-2	$(-1, -2)$
-2	$4 - 4 - 1$	-1	$(-2, -1)$
-3	$9 - 6 - 1$	$+2$	$(-3, +2)$
-4	$16 - 8 - 1$	$+7$	$(-4, +7)$

We can plot these solutions and sketch the parabola. See Figure 8.

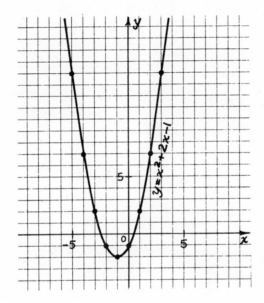

Figure 8

EXAMPLE 2 Graph the solution of $y = 2x^2 + 7x - 4$.

Since this is a quadratic equation, the graph is a parabola. Let's try 0, 1, 2, and 3 for x.

x	$2x^2 + 7x - 4$	y	Plot (x, y)
0	$0 + 0 - 4$	-4	$(0, -4)$
1	$2 + 7 - 4$	5	$(1, 5)$
2	$8 + 14 - 4$	18	$(2, 18)$
3	$18 + 21 - 4$	35	$(3, 35)$

We plot these solutions in Figure 9.

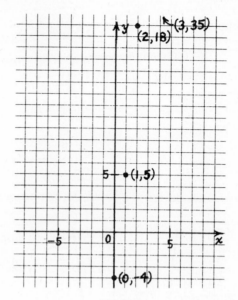

Figure 9

This looks like part of a parabola. Let's pick numbers for x that will give us more of a parabola. We'll put in -1, -2, -3, -4, and -5 for x.

x	$2x^2 + 7x - 4$	y	Plot (x, y)
-1	$2 - 7 - 4$	-9	$(-1, -9)$
-2	$8 - 14 - 4$	-10	$(-2, -10)$
-3	$18 - 21 - 4$	-7	$(-3, -7)$
-4	$32 - 28 - 4$	0	$(-4, 0)$
-5	$50 - 35 - 4$	11	$(-5, 11)$

Next we plot all these solutions and sketch the parabola. See Figure 10.

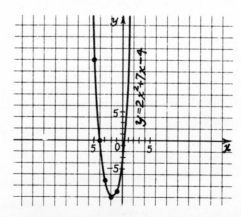

Figure 10

EXAMPLE 3   Graph the solution of $y = -x^2 + 4x + 2$.

Since this is a quadratic equation, the graph is a parabola. Let's try 0, 1, 2, and 3 for x.

x	$-x^2 + 4x + 2$	y	Plot (x, y)
0	$-0 +\ \ 0 + 2$	2	$(0, 2)$
1	$-1 +\ \ 4 + 2$	5	$(1, 5)$
2	$-4 +\ \ 8 + 2$	6	$(2, 6)$
3	$-9 + 12 + 2$	5	$(3, 5)$

Let's try these solutions in Figure 11.

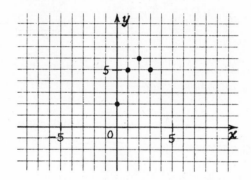

Figure 11

This looks like part of a parabola, so let's pick numbers for x to give us more of the parabola. We can pick -1 to get a little more of the left side, and we can pick 4 and 5 to get more of the right side.

x	$-x^2 + 4x + 2$	y	Plot (x, y)
-1	$-\ 1\ -\ \ 4 + 2$	-3	$(-1, -3)$
4	$-16 + 16 + 2$	2	$(4, 2)$
5	$-25 + 20 + 2$	-3	$(5, -3)$

Let's plot all these solutions and sketch the parabola. See Figure 12.

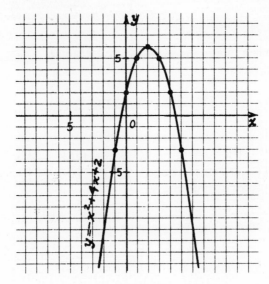

Figure 12

EXAMPLE 4 Graph the solution of $y = x^2$.

Since this is a quadratic equation, the graph is a parabola. Let's try 0, 1, 2, and 3 for x.

x	x^2	y	Plot (x, y)
0	0	0	$(0, 0)$
1	1	1	$(1, 1)$
2	4	4	$(2, 4)$
3	9	9	$(3, 9)$

Let's plot these solutions in Figure 13.

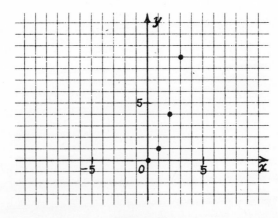

Figure 13

This looks like half a parabola. Let's pick numbers for x that will give us the other half.

x	x^2	y	Plot (x, y)
-1	1	1	$(-1, 1)$
-2	4	4	$(-2, 4)$
-3	9	9	$(-3, 9)$

Let's plot these solutions and sketch the parabola. See Figure 14.

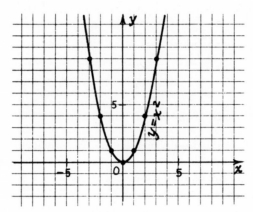

Figure 14

The parabolas we just graphed have one of two basic shapes. Each of the parabolas in Figures 5, 8, 10 and 14 opens upward and has a low point.

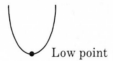

The parabola in Figure 12 opens downward and has a high point.

There is a way of determining the basic shape of a parabola and of locating its low or high point without plotting points. We do this directly from the equation. When the equation is in the standard form $y = ax^2 + bx + c$, then

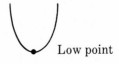

(1)   If a is positive, the graph opens upward.   Low point

(2)   If a is negative, the graph opens downward.   High point

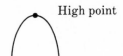

(3)   The x-coordinate of the low or high point is $\dfrac{-b}{2a}$.

We use this x-coordinate to calculate the y-coordinate.

EXAMPLE 5   Graph the solution of $y = x^2 + 4x + 5$.

This is a quadratic equation and its graph is a parabola. The equation is in standard form.

$$y = ax^2 + bx + c$$
$$y = 1x^2 + 4x + 5$$

So $a = 1$ and $b = 4$. (We don't need to use the c.)

Since a is positive, we know that the parabola opens upward and the graph has a low point. The x-coordinate of this low point is $\dfrac{-b}{2a}$.

For this parabola, a is 1 and b is 4, so the x-coordinate of the low point is $\dfrac{-4}{2(1)}$ or -2.

Now we will build a table of solutions. We put -2 in the center of the table, because we know the low point is in the center of the parabola.

x	$x^2 + 4x + 5$	y	(x, y) Solution
-4	$16 - 16 + 5$	5	$(-4, 5)$
-3	$9 - 12 + 5$	2	$(-3, 2)$
-2	$4 - 8 + 5$	1	$(-2, 1)$ Low point
-1	$1 - 4 + 5$	2	$(-1, 2)$
0	$0 + 0 + 5$	5	$(0, 5)$

We plot these solutions and sketch the parabola. See Figure 15.

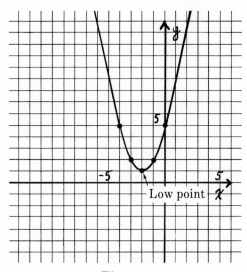

Figure 15

EXAMPLE 6 Without graphing, determine the general shape of the graph of $y = -4x^2 - 8x + 3$ and give the coordinates of its low or high point.

This is a quadratic equation and its graph is a parabola. The equation is in standard form.

$$y = \quad ax^2 + bx + c$$
$$y = -4x^2 - 8x + 3$$

So $a = -4$ and $b = -8$.

Since a is negative, we know that the parabola opens downward and the graph has a high point. The x-coordinate of this high point is $\dfrac{-b}{2a}$.

For this parabola, a is -4 and b is -8. So the x-coordinate of the high point is $\dfrac{-(-8)}{2(-4)}$ or $\dfrac{+8}{-8}$ or -1.

We calculate the y-coordinate of the high point.

x	$-4x^2 - 8x + 3$	y	High point
-1	$-4(-1)^2 - 8(-1) + 3$	7	$(-1, 7)$

So the graph of this equation is a parabola that opens downward. The coordinates of the high point are $(-1, 7)$.

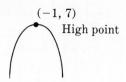
$(-1, 7)$
High point

Exercises

If 2 is put in place of x, find what must be put in place of y to make each of the following equations true.

1. $y = x^2 - x + 1$
2. $y = 3x^2 + 2x - 7$
3. $y = -x^2 + x - 1$
4. $y = -2x^2$
5. $y = -x^2 - x$

If -2 is put in place of x, find what must be put in place of y to make each of the following equations true.

6. $y = x^2 - x + 1$
7. $y = 3x^2 + 2x - 7$
8. $y = -x^2 + x - 1$
9. $y = -2x^2$
10. $y = -x^2 - x$

If 0 is put in place of x, find what must be put in place of y to make each of the following equations true.

11. $y = x^2 - x + 1$
12. $y = 3x^2 + 2x - 7$
13. $y = -x^2 + x - 1$
14. $y = -2x^2$
15. $y = -x^2 - x$

If 0 is put in place of y, find what must be put in place of x to make each of the following equations true.

16. $y = x^2 - 9$
17. $y = x^2 - 5x$
18. $y = (x + 1)(x - 2)$
19. $y = x^2 - 6x + 9$
20. $y = x^2 - 4x - 5$

Do the following problems.

21. Is $(2, -1)$ a solution of $y = x^2 - 5x + 4$?
22. Is $(-1, 4)$ a solution of $y = 2x^2 - 3x - 1$?
23. Is $(0, 3)$ a solution of $y = 5x^2 + 3$?
24. Is $(-5, 0)$ a solution of $y = x^2 - 5$?

Graph the solution of each of the following equations.

25. $y = x^2 - 2x - 3$
26. $y = x^2 + 2x - 15$
27. $y = x^2 + x - 2$
28. $y = 2x^2 - 3x + 1$
29. $y = x^2 + 5x + 5$
30. $y = -x^2 - 2x + 2$
31. $y = x^2 - 5x$
32. $y = x^2 - 9$
33. $y = -2x^2 + 3x - 5$
34. $y = 2x^2 + x - 6$
35. $2y = x^2$

Without graphing, determine the general shape of each of the following equations and give the coordinates of its low or high point.

36. $y = x^2 - 4x + 1$
37. $y = -3x^2 - 6x + 4$
38. $y = -x^2 + 8x - 5$
39. $y = 2x^2 + 12x$
40. $y = -4x^2 + 5$

Answers to Exercises

1. $y = x^2 - x + 1$
   $y = 2^2 - 2 + 1$
   $y = 4 - 2 + 1$
   $y = 3$

2. $y = 3x^2 + 2x - 7$
   $y = 3(2)^2 + 2(2) - 7$
   $y = 12 + 4 - 7$
   $y = 9$

3. $y = -x^2 + x - 1$
   $y = -(2)^2 + 2 - 1$
   $y = -4 + 2 - 1$
   $y = -3$

4. $y = -2x^2$
   $y = -2(2)^2$
   $y = -2(4)$
   $y = -8$

5. $y = -x^2 - x$
   $y = -(2)^2 - 2$
   $y = -4 - 2$
   $y = -6$

6. $y = x^2 - x + 1$
   $y = (-2)^2 - (-2) + 1$
   $y = 4 + 2 + 1$
   $y = 7$

7. $y = 3x^2 + 2x - 7$
   $y = 3(-2)^2 + 2(-2) - 7$
   $y = 12 - 4 - 7$
   $y = 1$

8. $y = -x^2 + x - 1$
   $y = -(-2)^2 + (-2) - 1$
   $y = -4 - 2 - 1$
   $y = -7$

9. $y = -2x^2$
   $y = -2(-2)^2$
   $y = -2(4)$
   $y = -8$

10. $y = -x^2 - x$
    $y = -(-2)^2 - (-2)$
    $y = -4 + 2$
    $y = -2$

11. $y = x^2 - x + 1$
    $y = 0^2 - 0 + 1$
    $y = 0 - 0 + 1$
    $y = +1$

12. $y = 3x^2 + 2x - 7$
    $y = 3(0)^2 + 2(0) - 7$
    $y = 0 + 0 - 7$
    $y = -7$

(13.) $y = -x^2 + x - 1$
$y = -(0)^2 + 0 - 1$
$y = 0 + 0 - 1$
$y = -1$

(19.) $y = x^2 - 6x + 9$
$0 = (x-3)(x-3)$
$x - 3 = 0$ $x - 3 = 0$
$x = 3$ $x = 3$

(14.) $y = -2x^2$
$y = -2(0)^2$
$y = -2(0)$
$y = 0$

(20.) $y = x^2 - 4x - 5$
$0 = (x-5)(x+1)$
$x - 5 = 0$ $x + 1 = 0$
$x = 5$ $x = -1$

(15.) $y = -x^2 - x$
$y = -0^2 - 0$
$y = -0 - 0$
$y = 0$

(21.) put in 2 for x and -1 for y
$y = x^2 - 5x + 4$
$-1 = 2^2 - 5(2) + 4$
$-1 = 4 - 10 + 4$
$-1 = -2$ NO

(16.) $y = x^2 - 9$
$0 = (x+3)(x-3)$
$x + 3 = 0$ $(x-3) = 0$
$x = -3$ $x = 3$

(22.) put in -1 for x and 4 for y
$y = 2x^2 - 3x - 1$
$4 = 2(-1)^2 - 3(-1) - 1$
$4 = 2 \cdot 1 + 3 - 1$
$4 = 4$ YES

(17.) $y = x^2 - 5x$
$0 = x(x-5)$
$x = 0$ $x - 5 = 0$
$x = 5$

(23.) put in 0 for x and 3 for y
$y = 5x^2 + 3$
$3 = 5(0)^2 + 3$
$3 = 5 \cdot 0 + 3$
$3 = 0 + 3$
$3 = 3$ YES

(18.) $y = (x+1)(x-2)$
$0 = (x+1)(x-2)$
$x + 1 = 0$ $x - 2 = 0$
$x = -1$ $x = 2$

24.) put in -5 for x and 0 for y

$y = x^2 - 5$

$0 = (-5)^2 - 5$

$0 = 25 - 5$

$0 = 20$ NO

28.)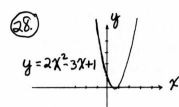

$y = 2x^2 - 3x + 1$

25.)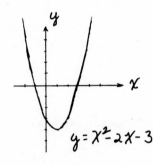

$y = x^2 - 2x - 3$

29.)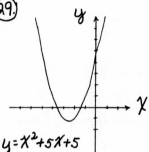

$y = x^2 + 5x + 5$

26.)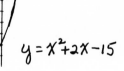

$y = x^2 + 2x - 15$

30.)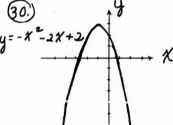

$y = -x^2 - 2x + 2$

31.)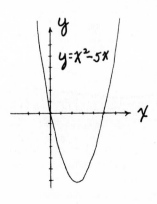

$y = x^2 - 5x$

27.)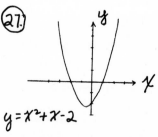

$y = x^2 + x - 2$

32.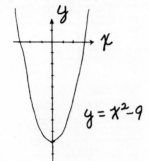

$y = x^2 - 9$

33.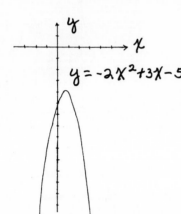

$y = -2x^2 + 3x - 5$

34.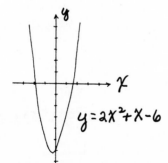

$y = 2x^2 + x - 6$

35.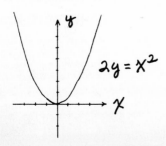

$2y = x^2$

36.

$(2, -3)$
Low point

37. High point
$(-1, 7)$

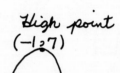

38. High point
$(4, 11)$

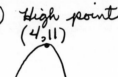

39.

$(-3, -18)$
Low point

40. High point
$(0, 5)$

Additional Exercises

If 3 is put in place of x, find what must be put in place of y to make each of the following equations true.

1. $y = x^2 + x + 2$
2. $y = 2x^2 + 3x + 1$
3. $y = 3x^2 - 4x + 3$
4. $y = -5x^2$
5. $y = -x^2 - 4x - 2$

If -3 is put in place of x, find what must be put in place of y to make each of the following equations true.

6. $y = x^2 + x + 2$
7. $y = 2x^2 + 3x + 1$
8. $y = 3x^2 - 4x + 3$
9. $y = -5x^2$
10. $y = -x^2 - 4x - 2$

If 0 is put in place of x, find what must be put in place of y to make each of the following equations true.

11. $y = x^2 + x + 2$
12. $y = 2x^2 + 3x + 1$
13. $y = 3x^2 - 4x + 3$
14. $y = -5x^2$
15. $y = -x^2 - 4x - 2$

If 0 is put in place of y, find what must be put in place of x to make each of the following equations true.

16. $y = x^2 - 25$
17. $y = x^2 - 3x$
18. $y = (x + 4)(x - 3)$
19. $y = x^2 - 8x + 16$
20. $y = x^2 - x - 6$

Do the following problems.

21. Is $(-1, 9)$ a solution of $y = x^2 - 3x + 5$?
22. Is $(2, -1)$ a solution of $y = 3x^2 - 4x - 1$?
23. Is $(0, 2)$ a solution of $y = 4x^2 + 2$?
24. Is $(-3, 0)$ a solution of $y = x^2 - 3$?

Graph the solution of each of the following equations.

25. $y = x^2 - 3x - 4$
26. $y = x^2 + 2x - 8$
27. $y = x^2 - x - 2$
28. $y = 3x^2 + 4x + 1$
29. $y = x^2 + 3x + 3$
30. $y = -x^2 - 3x + 1$
31. $y = x^2 - 4x$
32. $y = x^2 - 4$
33. $y = -3x^2 + 2x - 1$
34. $y = 2x^2 + 3x - 2$
35. $3y = x^2$

Without graphing, determine the general shape of the graph of each of the following equations, and give the coordinates of its low or high point.

36. $y = x^2 - 6x + 2$
37. $y = -2x^2 - 8x + 2$
38. $y = -x^2 + 4x + 1$
39. $y = 3x^2 - 12x + 3$
40. $y = -5x^2 + 7$

Simultaneous Solutions of Equations by Graphing

Let's graph the solutions of two equations on the same picture.

EXAMPLE 1   Graph $y = x^2 - 2x - 3$ and $y = 2x - 7$ on the same picture.

Note: Since $y = x^2 - 2x - 3$ is in the form $y = ax^2 + bx + c$, its graph is a parabola. Since $y = 2x - 7$ is in the form $y = mx + b$, its graph is a straight line.

Let's graph the parabola first. Since a is positive, the parabola opens upward. The x-coordinate of the low point is

$$\frac{-b}{2a} = \frac{-(-2)}{2(1)} \quad \text{or} \quad 1.$$

x	$x^2 - 2x - 3$	y	Plot (x, y)	
4	$16 - 8 \ - 3$	5	$(4, 5)$	
3	$9 - 6 \ - 3$	0	$(3, 0)$	
2	$4 - 4 \ - 3$	-3	$(2, -3)$	
1	$1 - 2 \ - 3$	-4	$(1, -4)$	Low point
0	$0 - 0 \ - 3$	-3	$(0, -3)$	
-1	$1 + 2 \ - 3$	0	$(-1, 0)$	
-2	$4 + 4 \ - 3$	5	$(-2, 5)$	

The graph is sketched in Figure 1.

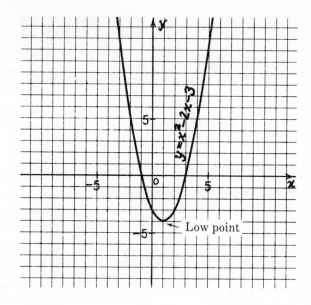

Figure 1

Now let's graph the straight line $y = 2x - 7$ on the same picture.
See Figure 2.

x	$2x - 7$	y	Plot (x, y)
-1	$-2 - 7$	-9	$(-1, -9)$
0	$0 - 7$	-7	$(0, -7)$
1	$2 - 7$	-5	$(1, -5)$
2	$4 - 7$	-3	$(2, -3)$

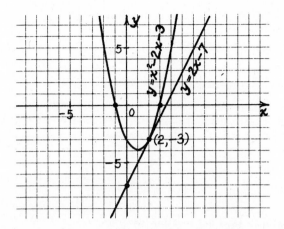

Figure 2

Note: In Figure 2 the two graphs meet at the point (2, −3). Since (2, −3) is on the graph of the parabola, it is a solution of the equation $y = x^2 - 2x - 3$. Also, since (2, −3) is on the graph of the straight line, it is a solution of $y = 2x - 7$.

We call a point which is the solution of two different equations the **simultaneous solution** of the two equations. Although there are many solutions of the first equation and many solutions of the second equation, (2, −3) is a point that is a simultaneous solution of both equations. That is, (2, −3) makes $y = x^2 - 2x - 3$ true and (2, −3) also makes $y = 2x - 7$ true. Since these two graphs touch only once, (2, −3) is the only simultaneous solution of the equations $y = x^2 - 2x - 3$ and $y = 2x - 7$. To check this solution we put in 2 for x and −3 for y in each equation.

$$
\begin{array}{ll}
y = x^2 - 2x\ - 3 & \qquad y = 2x\ - 7 \\
-3 = 2^2 - 2(2) - 3 & \qquad -3 = 2(2) - 7 \\
-3 = 4\ - 4\ - 3 & \qquad -3 = 4\ - 7 \\
-3 = -3 \quad \underline{\text{True}} & \qquad -3 = -3 \quad \underline{\text{True}}
\end{array}
$$

So (2, −3) is the simultaneous solution of both equations.

EXAMPLE 2   Find the simultaneous solution of $y = x^2 - 6x + 8$ and $y = x + 2$ by graphing.

Let's graph the parabola first. Since a is positive, the parabola opens upward. The x-coordinate of the low point is

$$\frac{-b}{2a} = \frac{-(-6)}{2(1)} \quad \text{or} \quad 3.$$

x	$x^2 - 6x + 8$	y	Plot (x, y)	
0	$0 - \;\;0 + 8$	8	(0, 8)	
1	$1 - \;\;6 + 8$	3	(1, 3)	
2	$4 - 12 + 8$	0	(2, 0)	
3	$9 - 18 + 8$	-1	(3, -1)	Low point
4	$16 - 24 + 8$	0	(4, 0)	
5	$25 - 30 + 8$	3	(5, 3)	
6	$36 - 36 + 8$	8	(6, 8)	

The graph is sketched below.

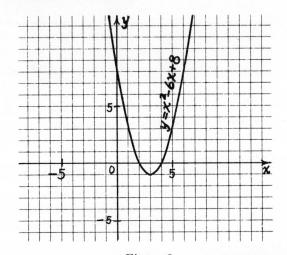

Figure 3

Now let's graph the straight line $y = x + 2$ on the same picture.
See Figure 4.

x	$x + 2$	y	Plot (x, y)
0	$0 + 2$	2	(0, 2)
1	$1 + 2$	3	(1, 3)
2	$2 + 2$	4	(2, 4)
3	$3 + 2$	5	(3, 5)

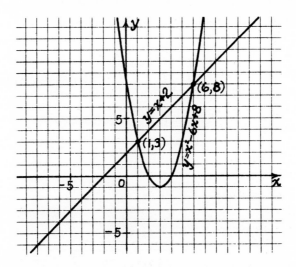

Figure 4

Notice that the graphs cross at <u>two</u> points (1, 3) and (6, 8). So there are two simultaneous solutions of the equations $y = x^2 - 6x + 8$ and $y = x + 2$. To check that (1, 3) is a simultaneous solution, we put in 1 for x and 3 for y in each equation.

$$\begin{array}{ll} y = x^2 - 6x + 8 & \quad y = x + 2 \\ 3 = 1 - 6 + 8 & \quad 3 = 1 + 2 \\ 3 = 3 \quad \underline{\text{True}} & \quad 3 = 3 \quad \underline{\text{True}} \end{array}$$

To check that (6, 8) is a simultaneous solution, we put 6 in for x and 8 in for y.

$$\begin{array}{ll} y = x^2 - 6x + 8 & \quad y = x + 2 \\ 8 = 36 - 36 + 8 & \quad 8 = 6 + 2 \\ 8 = 8 \quad \underline{\text{True}} & \quad 8 = 8 \quad \underline{\text{True}} \end{array}$$

So (1, 3) and (6, 8) are the two simultaneous solutions of both equations. Since these two graphs cross <u>twice</u>, (1, 3) and (6, 8) are the <u>only</u> simultaneous solutions of $y = x^2 - 6x + 8$ and $y = x + 2$.

EXAMPLE 3   Find the simultaneous solution of $y = x^2 - 1$ and $y = x - 5$ by graphing.

Let's graph the parabola first. Since a is positive, the parabola opens upward. The x-coordinate of the low point is

$$\frac{-b}{2a} = \frac{0}{2(1)} \quad \text{or} \quad 0.$$

x	$x^2 - 1$	y	Plot (x, y)	
3	$9 - 1$	8	$(3, 8)$	
2	$4 - 1$	3	$(2, 3)$	
1	$1 - 1$	0	$(1, 0)$	
0	$0 - 1$	-1	$(0, -1)$	Low point
-1	$1 - 1$	0	$(-1, 0)$	
-2	$4 - 1$	3	$(-2, 3)$	
-3	$9 - 1$	8	$(-3, 8)$	

The graph is sketched below.

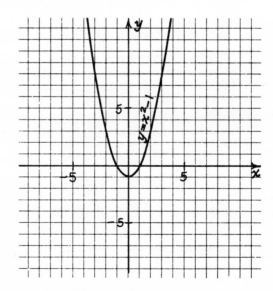

Figure 5

Now let's graph the straight line $y = x - 5$ on the same picture. See Figure 6.

x	$x - 5$	y	Plot (x, y)
0	$0 - 5$	-5	$(0, -5)$
1	$1 - 5$	-4	$(1, -4)$
2	$2 - 5$	-3	$(2, -3)$
3	$3 - 5$	-2	$(3, -2)$

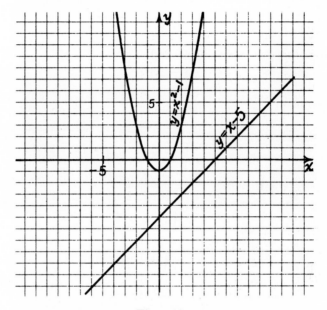

Figure 6

Notice that the graphs do not cross. They never cross! So even though there are many solutions of the first equation and many solutions of the second equation, there is no real simultaneous solution of the two equations $y = x^2 - 1$ and $y = x - 5$.

EXAMPLE 4   Find the simultaneous solution of $y = x^2$ and $y = x$ by graphing.

Let's graph the parabola first. Since a is positive, the parabola opens upward. The x-coordinate of the low point is

$$\frac{-b}{2a} = \frac{0}{2(1)} \quad \text{or} \quad 0.$$

x	x^2	y	Plot (x, y)	
3	9	9	(3, 9)	
2	4	4	(2, 4)	
1	1	1	(1, 1)	
0	0	0	(0, 0)	Low point
−1	1	1	(−1, 1)	
−2	4	4	(−2, 4)	
−3	9	9	(−3, 9)	

The graph is sketched below.

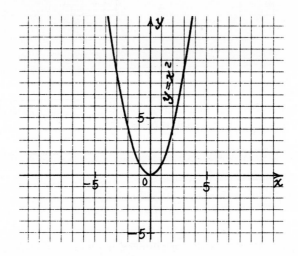

Figure 7

Now let's graph the straight line $y = x$ on the same picture. See Figure 8.

x	y
0	0
1	1
2	2
3	3

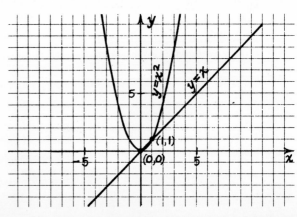

Figure 8

Notice that the graphs cross at two points (1, 1) and (0, 0). So there are two simultaneous solutions of the equations $y = x^2$ and $y = x$. To check that (1, 1) is a simultaneous solution, we put in 1 for x and 1 for y in each equation.

$$y = x^2 \qquad\qquad y = x$$
$$1 = 1^2 \qquad\qquad 1 = 1 \qquad \text{True}$$
$$1 = 1 \qquad \text{True}$$

To check that (0, 0) is a simultaneous solution, we put in 0 for x and 0 for y in each equation.

$$y = x^2 \qquad\qquad y = x$$
$$0 = 0^2 \qquad\qquad 0 = 0 \quad \text{True}$$
$$0 = 0 \qquad \text{True}$$

So (1, 1) and (0, 0) are the two simultaneous solutions of both equations.

EXAMPLE 5 Find the simultaneous solution of $y = x^2 - 4$ and $y = -x^2 + 4$ by graphing.

These are both parabolas. Let's graph the parabola $y = x^2 - 4$ first. Since a is positive, it opens upward. The x-coordinate of the low point is $\dfrac{-b}{2a} = \dfrac{0}{2(1)}$ or 0.

x	$x^2 - 4$	y	Plot (x, y)	
3	9 − 4	5	(3, 5)	
2	4 − 4	0	(2, 0)	
1	1 − 4	−3	(1, −3)	
0	0 − 4	−4	(0, −4)	Low point
−1	1 − 4	−3	(−1, −3)	
−2	4 − 4	0	(−2, 0)	
−3	9 − 4	5	(−3, 5)	

The graph is sketched on the next page in Figure 9.

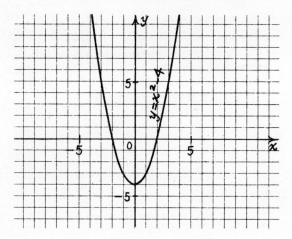

Figure 9

Now let's graph the parabola $y = -x^2 + 4$ on the same picture. Since a is negative, it opens downward. The x-coordinate of the high point is

$$\frac{-b}{2a} = \frac{0}{2(-1)} \quad \text{or} \quad 0. \text{ See Figure 10.}$$

x	$-x^2 + 4$	y	Plot (x, y)	
3	$-9 + 4$	-5	$(3, -5)$	
2	$-4 + 4$	0	$(2, 0)$	
1	$-1 + 4$	3	$(1, 3)$	
0	$0 + 4$	4	$(0, 4)$	High point
-1	$-1 + 4$	3	$(-1, 3)$	
-2	$-4 + 4$	0	$(-2, 0)$	
-3	$-9 + 4$	-5	$(-3, -5)$	

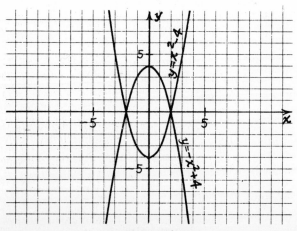

Figure 10

Notice that the graphs cross at two points $(2, 0)$ and $(-2, 0)$. So there are two simultaneous solutions of the equations $y = x^2 - 4$ and $y = -x^2 + 4$. To check that $(2, 0)$ is a simultaneous solution, we put in 2 for x and 0 for y in each equation.

$$y = x^2 - 4 \qquad\qquad y = -x^2 + 4$$
$$0 = 2^2 - 4 \qquad\qquad 0 = -(2)^2 + 4$$
$$0 = 4 - 4 \qquad\qquad 0 = -4 + 4$$
$$0 = 0 \quad \text{True} \qquad\qquad 0 = 0 \quad \text{True}$$

To check that $(-2, 0)$ is a simultaneous solution, we put in -2 for x and 0 for y in each equation.

$$y = x^2 - 4 \qquad\qquad y = -x^2 + 4$$
$$0 = (-2)^2 - 4 \qquad\qquad 0 = -(-2)^2 + 4$$
$$0 = 4 - 4 \qquad\qquad 0 = -4 + 4$$
$$0 = 0 \quad \text{True} \qquad\qquad 0 = 0 \quad \text{True}$$

So $(2, 0)$ and $(-2, 0)$ are the two simultaneous solutions of both equations.

Exercises

Find all simultaneous solutions of each pair of equations by graphing.

1. $y = x^2 - 5x + 4$
    $y = x - 5$
2. $y = x^2 - 4x + 3$
    $y = 2x - 6$
3. $y = x^2 - 2x - 3$
    $y = x + 1$
4. $y = x^2 + 4x + 3$
    $y = x + 1$
5. $y = x^2 - 2x$
    $y = x - 2$
6. $y = x^2 - 2$
    $y = 2x - 3$
7. $y = x^2 - 1$
    $y = x - 4$
8. $y = x^2$
    $y = x + 2$
9. $y = x^2$
    $y = -x^2$
10. $y = x^2 - 1$
    $y = -x^2 + 1$

Answers to Exercises

①

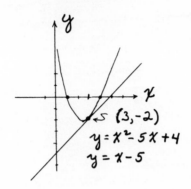

$(3,-2)$
$y = x^2 - 5x + 4$
$y = x - 5$

④

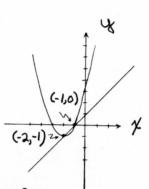

$(-1,0)$
$(-2,-1)$
$y = x^2 + 4x + 3$
$y = x + 1$

②

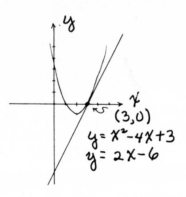

$(3,0)$
$y = x^2 - 4x + 3$
$y = 2x - 6$

⑤

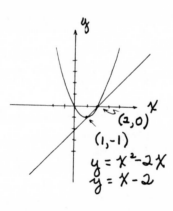

$(2,0)$
$(1,-1)$
$y = x^2 - 2x$
$y = x - 2$

③

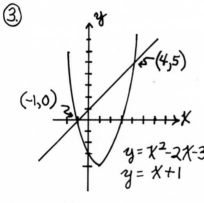

$(4,5)$
$(-1,0)$
$y = x^2 - 2x - 3$
$y = x + 1$

⑥

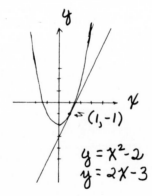

$(1,-1)$
$y = x^2 - 2$
$y = 2x - 3$

⑦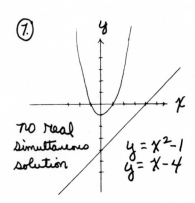

no real
simultaneous
solution

$y = x^2 - 1$
$y = x - 4$

⑩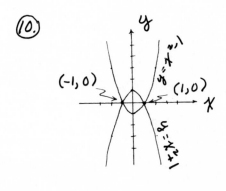

$(-1, 0)$ $(1, 0)$

$y = x^2 - 1$

$y = -x^2 + 1$

⑧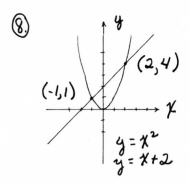

$(2, 4)$

$(-1, 1)$

$y = x^2$
$y = x + 2$

⑨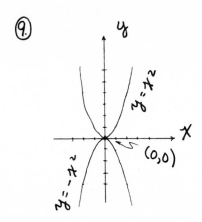

$y = x^2$

$y = -x^2$

$(0, 0)$

Additional Exercises

Find all simultaneous solutions of each pair of equations by graphing.

1. $y = x^2 - 3x + 2$
   $y = x - 2$

2. $y = x^2 - 5x + 6$
   $y = x - 3$

3. $y = x^2 + x - 2$
   $y = x + 2$

4. $y = x^2 - 7x + 10$
   $y = x + 3$

5. $y = x^2 - 3x$
   $y = x - 3$

6. $y = x^2 - 3$
   $y = x - 4$

7. $y = x^2 - 4$
   $y = x - 6$

8. $y = x^2$
   $y = -x$

9. $y = -x^2$
   $y = x$

10. $y = x^2 - 9$
    $y = -x^2 + 9$

Lesson 6

Simultaneous Solutions of Equations by Algebra

When we use the graphing method to get simultaneous solutions of equations, it is sometimes difficult to decide where the graphs actually cross. In Figure 1, points A and B are the simultaneous solutions, but we are not sure of their exact coordinates. We can get the exact solutions if we use algebra.

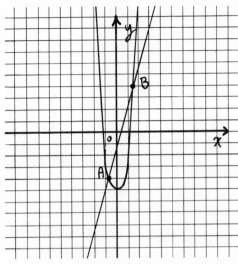

Figure 1

EXAMPLE 1   Find the simultaneous solution of the following two equations algebraically: $y = 4x^2 - 5$ and $y = 4x - 2$

If there is a point (x, y) that makes both equations true, then for that point the y's on the left side both stand for the same number. So the right sides are equal to each other, because if two things are equal to the same thing, then they are equal to each other. We write

$$4x^2 - 5 = 4x - 2$$

Let's solve this equation.

$$
\begin{array}{rll}
 & 4x^2 - 5 = & 4x - 2 \\
\text{Add } -4x & \underline{-4x} & \underline{-4x} \\
 & 4x^2 - 4x - 5 = & -2 \\
\text{Add } +2 & \underline{+2} & \underline{+2} \\
 & 4x^2 - 4x - 3 = & 0
\end{array}
$$

Now we can solve this quadratic equation by factoring.

$$(2x - 3)(2x + 1) = 0$$

$$
\begin{array}{c|c}
\begin{aligned}
2x - 3 &= 0 \\
2x &= 3 \\
x &= \frac{3}{2}
\end{aligned}
&
\begin{aligned}
2x + 1 &= 0 \\
2x &= -1 \\
x &= -\frac{1}{2}
\end{aligned}
\end{array}
$$

These are the x-coordinates of the two simultaneous solutions. Now, to find the y-coordinate of each solution, we go back to either one of the original equations. We will go back to $y = 4x - 2$ because it is simpler.

$$
\begin{array}{c|c}
y = 4x - 2 & y = 4x - 2 \\
\\
\text{Put } \dfrac{3}{2} \text{ in for } x. & \text{Put } -\dfrac{1}{2} \text{ in for } x. \\
\\
y = 4\left(\dfrac{3}{2}\right) - 2 & y = 4\left(-\dfrac{1}{2}\right) - 2 \\
y = 6 - 2 & y = -2 - 2 \\
y = 4 & y = -4 \\
\\
\left(\dfrac{3}{2}, 4\right) \text{ is a solution.} & \left(-\dfrac{1}{2}, -4\right) \text{ is a solution.}
\end{array}
$$

So the two solutions of $y = 4x^2 - 5$ and $y = 4x - 2$ are $\left(\dfrac{3}{2}, 4\right)$ and $\left(-\dfrac{1}{2}, -4\right)$. To check, we put $\left(\dfrac{3}{2}, 4\right)$ and $\left(-\dfrac{1}{2}, -4\right)$ into both equations.

For the solution $\left(\dfrac{3}{2}, 4\right)$ we get the following.

$$y = 4x^2 - 5 \qquad\qquad y = 4x - 2$$
$$4 = 4\left(\dfrac{3}{2}\right)^2 - 5 \qquad\qquad 4 = 4\left(\dfrac{3}{2}\right) - 2$$
$$4 = 4\left(\dfrac{9}{4}\right) - 5 \qquad\qquad 4 = 6 - 2$$
$$\qquad\qquad\qquad\qquad 4 = 4 \quad \underline{\text{True}}$$
$$4 = 9 - 5$$
$$4 = 4 \quad \underline{\text{True}}$$

So the simultaneous solution $\left(\dfrac{3}{2}, 4\right)$ checks.

For the solution $\left(-\dfrac{1}{2}, -4\right)$ we get the following.

$$y = 4x^2 - 5 \qquad\qquad y = 4x - 2$$
$$-4 = 4\left(-\dfrac{1}{2}\right)^2 - 5 \qquad\qquad -4 = 4\left(-\dfrac{1}{2}\right) - 2$$
$$-4 = 4\left(\dfrac{1}{4}\right) - 5 \qquad\qquad -4 = -2 - 2$$
$$\qquad\qquad\qquad\qquad -4 = -4 \quad \underline{\text{True}}$$
$$-4 = 1 - 5$$
$$-4 = -4 \quad \underline{\text{True}}$$

So the simultaneous solution $\left(-\dfrac{1}{2}, -4\right)$ checks.

EXAMPLE 2 Find the simultaneous solution of the following two equations algebraically: $y = x^2 - 1$ and $y = x + 5$

If there is a simultaneous solution, then

$$x^2 - 1 = x + 5$$

Let's solve this equation.

$$
\begin{array}{rcl}
x^2 - 1 & = & x + 5 \\
-\,x & & -\,x \\
\hline
x^2 - x - 1 & = & 5 \\
-\,5 & & -5 \\
\hline
x^2 - x - 6 & = & 0
\end{array}
$$

Now we can factor $x^2 - x - 6 = 0$, and get $(x - 3)(x + 2) = 0$.

$$x - 3 = 0 \qquad x + 2 = 0$$
$$x = 3 \qquad\quad x = -2$$

These are the x-coordinates of the two simultaneous solutions. Now, to find the y-coordinate of each solution, we go back to either one of the original equations. We will use the equation $y = x + 5$ because it is simpler.

$y = x + 5$ $y = x + 5$

Put 3 in for x.   Put in -2 for x.

$y = 3 + 5$ $y = -2 + 5$
$y = 8$ $y = 3$

(3, 8) is a solution. $(-2, 3)$ is a solution.

So the two simultaneous solutions of $y = x^2 - 1$ and $y = x + 5$ are (3, 8) and $(-2, 3)$. To check, we put (3, 8) and $(-2, 3)$ into both equations.

For the solution (3, 8) we get the following.

$y = x^2 - 1$ $y = x + 5$
$8 = 3^2 - 1$ $8 = 3 + 5$
$8 = 9 - 1$ $8 = 8$ $\quad$ <u>True</u>
$8 = 8$ $\quad$ <u>True</u>

So the simultaneous solution (3, 8) checks.

For the solution $(-2, 3)$ we get the following.

$y = x^2 - 1$ $y = x + 5$
$3 = (-2)^2 - 1$ $3 = -2 + 5$
$3 = 4 - 1$ $3 = 3$ $\quad$ <u>True</u>
$3 = 3$ $\quad$ <u>True</u>

So the simultaneous solution $(-2, 3)$ checks.

EXAMPLE 3   Find the simultaneous solution of the following two equations algebraically: $y = x^2 - 2x - 3$ and $y = 2x - 7$

If there is a simultaneous solution, then

$$x^2 - 2x - 3 = 2x - 7$$

Let's solve this equation.

$$
\begin{array}{rcr}
x^2 - 2x - 3 & = & 2x - 7 \\
- 2x & & -2x \\
\hline
x^2 - 4x - 3 & = & -7 \\
+ 7 & & +7 \\
\hline
x^2 - 4x + 4 & = & 0
\end{array}
$$

Now we can factor $x^2 - 4x + 4 = 0$, and get $(x - 2)(x - 2) = 0$.

$$
\begin{aligned}
x - 2 &= 0 \\
x &= 2
\end{aligned}
$$

There is only one solution. So the x-coordinate of the simultaneous solution is 2. Now, to find the y-coordinate of the solution, go back to either one of the original equations and put 2 in for x.

$$y = 2x - 7$$

Put 2 in for x.

$$
\begin{aligned}
y &= 2(2) - 7 \\
y &= 4 - 7 \\
y &= -3
\end{aligned}
$$

$(2, -3)$ is a solution.

So the only simultaneous solution of $y = x^2 - 2x - 3$ and $y = 2x - 7$ is $(2, -3)$.

Note: In example 1 of Lesson 5 these equations were solved by graphing.

EXAMPLE 4   Find the simultaneous solution of the following two equations algebraically: $y = x^2 - 2x + 1$ and $y = x^2 - x - 2$

If there is a simultaneous solution, then

$$x^2 - 2x + 1 = x^2 - x - 2$$

Let's solve this equation.

$$
\begin{array}{rcl}
x^2 - 2x + 1 &=& x^2 - x - 2 \\
-x^2 & & -x^2 \\
\hline
-2x + 1 &=& -x - 2 \\
+2x & & +2x \\
\hline
1 &=& x - 2 \\
+2 & & +2 \\
\hline
3 &=& x
\end{array}
$$

This is the x-coordinate of the solution. Now, to find the y-coordinate of the solution, we go back to either one of the original equations.

$$y = x^2 - 2x + 1$$

Put 3 in for x.

$$y = (3)^2 - 2(3) + 1$$
$$y = 9 - 6 + 1$$
$$y = 4$$

(3, 4) is a solution.

So the only simultaneous solution of $y = x^2 - 2x + 1$ and $y = x^2 - x - 2$ is (3, 4).

EXAMPLE 5   Find the simultaneous solution of the following two equations algebraically: $y = x^2 - 4$ and $y = -x^2 + 4$

If there is a simultaneous solution, then

$$x^2 - 4 = -x^2 + 4$$

Let's solve this equation.

$$x^2 - 4 = -x^2 + 4$$
$$\underline{+x^2 \qquad\qquad +x^2}$$
$$2x^2 - 4 = \qquad\quad 4$$
$$\underline{\quad - 4 \qquad\qquad - 4}$$
$$2x^2 - 8 = \qquad 0$$

Now we can factor this quadratic equation. We get

$$2(x^2 - 4) = 0$$
$$2(x + 2)(x - 2) = 0$$

$$x + 2 = 0 \qquad\quad x - 2 = 0$$
$$\qquad x = -2 \qquad\qquad x = 2$$

These are the x-coordinates of the two simultaneous solutions. Now, to find the y-coordinate of each solution, we go back to either one of the original equations.

$y = x^2 - 4$	$y = x^2 - 4$
Put -2 in for x.	Put 2 in for x.
$y = (-2)^2 - 4$	$y = 2^2 - 4$
$y = 4 - 4$	$y = 4 - 4$
$y = 0$	$y = 0$
$(-2, 0)$ is a solution.	$(2, 0)$ is a solution.

So the simultaneous solutions of $y = x^2 - 4$ and $y = -x^2 + 4$ are $(-2, 0)$ and $(2, 0)$.

Note: In example 5 of Lesson 5 these equations are solved by graphing.

EXAMPLE 6 Find the simultaneous solution of the following two equations algebraically: $y = x^2 + 3x + 2$ and $y = 3x + 5$

If there is a simultaneous solution, then

$$x^2 + 3x + 2 = 3x + 5$$

Let's solve this equation.

$$\begin{array}{rcl} x^2 + 3x + 2 &=& 3x + 5 \\ -3x & & -3x \\ \hline x^2 + 2 &=& 5 \\ -5 & & -5 \\ \hline x^2 - 3 &=& 0 \end{array}$$

Now we can use the quadratic formulas.

$$a = 1, b = 0, c = -3$$

$$x = \frac{-b + \sqrt{b^2 - 4ac}}{2a} \qquad x = \frac{-b - \sqrt{b^2 - 4ac}}{2a}$$

$$x = \frac{0 + \sqrt{0 - 4(1)(-3)}}{2(1)} \qquad x = \frac{0 - \sqrt{0 - 4(1)(-3)}}{2(1)}$$

$$x = \frac{\sqrt{12}}{2} \qquad x = \frac{-\sqrt{12}}{2}$$

$$x = \frac{\sqrt{4 \cdot 3}}{2} \qquad x = \frac{-\sqrt{4 \cdot 3}}{2}$$

$$x = \frac{2\sqrt{3}}{2} \qquad x = \frac{-2\sqrt{3}}{2}$$

$$x = \sqrt{3} \qquad x = -\sqrt{3}$$

These are the x-coordinates of the two simultaneous solutions. Now, to find the y-coordinate of each solution, we go back to either one of the original equations.

$$y = 3x + 5 \qquad\qquad\qquad y = 3x + 5$$

Put $\sqrt{3}$ in for x. $\qquad\qquad$ Put $-\sqrt{3}$ in for x.

$$y = 3\sqrt{3} + 5 \qquad\qquad\qquad y = -3\sqrt{3} + 5$$

$(\sqrt{3}, 3\sqrt{3} + 5)$ is a solution. $\qquad$ $(-\sqrt{3}, -3\sqrt{3} + 5)$ is a solution.

So the two simultaneous solutions of $y = x^2 + 3x + 2$ and $y = 3x + 5$ are $(\sqrt{3}, 3\sqrt{3} + 5)$ and $(-\sqrt{3}, -3\sqrt{3} + 5)$.

EXAMPLE 7   Find the simultaneous solution of the following two equations algebraically: $y = x^2 - 1$ and $y = x - 5$

If there is a simultaneous solution, then

$$x^2 - 1 = x - 5$$

Let's solve this equation.

$$
\begin{array}{rcr}
x^2 \qquad - 1 = & & x - 5 \\
- x & & -x \\
\hline
x^2 - x - 1 = & & - 5 \\
+ 5 & & + 5 \\
\hline
x^2 - x + 4 = & & 0
\end{array}
$$

This quadratic equation cannot be factored, so we use the quadratic formulas.

$$a = 1,\ b = -1,\ c = 4$$

$$x = \frac{-b + \sqrt{b^2 - 4ac}}{2a} \qquad\qquad x = \frac{-b - \sqrt{b^2 - 4ac}}{2a}$$

$$x = \frac{-(-1) + \sqrt{(-1)^2 - 4(1)(4)}}{2(1)} \qquad x = \frac{-1(-1) - \sqrt{(-1)^2 - 4(1)(4)}}{2(1)}$$

$$x = \frac{1 + \sqrt{1 - 16}}{2} \qquad\qquad x = \frac{1 - \sqrt{1 - 16}}{2}$$

$$x = \frac{1 + \sqrt{-15}}{2} \qquad\qquad x = \frac{1 - \sqrt{-15}}{2}$$

Note: Each of these numbers contains $\sqrt{-15}$, which is not a real number. So there are no real simultaneous solutions of $y = x^2 - 1$ and $y = x - 5$. In example 3 of Lesson 5, we found that the graphs of these equations do not cross. Graphs will cross only if there are real simultaneous solutions.

Exercises

Find all the simultaneous solutions of each pair of equations algebraically.

1. $y = x^2 - 5x + 6$
   $y = x + 1$
2. $y = x^2 - 6x + 9$
   $y = x + 3$
3. $y = x^2 - 3$
   $y = x + 3$
4. $y = x^2 - 9$
   $y = 3x + 1$
5. $y = x^2 + 6x + 9$
   $y = 2x + 5$
6. $y = x^2 - 2x + 1$
   $y = 3x - 5$
7. $y = x^2 - 3x + 2$
   $y = x^2 - 4x + 3$
8. $y = x^2 - 9$
   $y = -x^2 + 9$
9. $y = x^2 + 4x + 3$
   $y = 4x + 8$
10. $y = x^2 - 3$
    $y = x - 6$
11. $y = 3x^2 + 1$
    $y = 7x - 3$

Answers to Exercises

(1.) $x^2 - 5x + 6 = x + 1$
$\underline{\quad -x \qquad\quad -x}$
$x^2 - 6x + 6 = \qquad +1$
$\underline{\qquad\quad -1 \qquad -1}$
$x^2 - 6x + 5 = \qquad 0$

$(x - 5)(x - 1) = 0$
$x - 5 = 0 \quad x - 1 = 0$
$\quad x = 5 \qquad x = 1$

$y = x + 1 \qquad y = x + 1$
$y = 5 + 1 \qquad y = 1 + 1$
$y = 6 \qquad\quad y = 2$
solutions are $(5, 6)$ and $(1, 2)$

(3.) $x^2 + 0x - 3 = x + 3$
$\underline{\quad -x \qquad\quad -x}$
$x^2 - x - 3 = \qquad +3$
$\underline{\qquad\quad -3 \qquad -3}$
$x^2 - x - 6 = \qquad 0$

$(x + 2)(x - 3) = 0$
$x + 2 = 0 \qquad x - 3 = 0$
$\quad x = -2 \qquad\quad x = 3$

$y = x + 3 \qquad y = x + 3$
$y = -2 + 3 \qquad y = 3 + 3$
$y = 1 \qquad\quad y = 6$
solutions are $(-2, 1)$ and $(3, 6)$

(2.) $x^2 - 6x + 9 = x + 3$
$\underline{\quad -x \qquad\quad -x}$
$x^2 - 7x + 9 = \qquad +3$
$\underline{\qquad\quad -3 \qquad -3}$
$x^2 - 7x + 6 = \qquad 0$

$(x - 6)(x - 1) = 0$
$x - 6 = 0 \qquad x - 1 = 0$
$\quad x = 6 \qquad\quad x = 1$

$y = x + 3 \qquad y = x + 3$
$y = 6 + 3 \qquad y = 1 + 3$
$y = 9 \qquad\quad y = 4$
solutions are $(6, 9)$ and $(1, 4)$

(4.) $x^2 - 9 = 3x + 1$
$x^2 + 0x - 9 = 3x + 1$
$\underline{\quad -3x \qquad -3x}$
$x^2 - 3x - 9 = \qquad +1$
$\underline{\qquad\quad -1 \qquad -1}$
$x^2 - 3x - 10 = 0$

$(x + 2)(x - 5) = 0$
$x + 2 = 0 \qquad x - 5 = 0$
$\quad x = -2 \qquad\quad x = 5$

$y = 3x + 1 \qquad y = 3x + 1$
$y = 3(-2) + 1 \qquad y = 3(5) + 1$
$y = -6 + 1 \qquad y = 15 + 1$
$y = -5 \qquad\quad y = 16$
solutions are $(-2, -5)$ and $(5, 16)$

⑤ $x^2 + 6x + 9 = 2x + 5$

$\underline{\quad -2x \qquad -2x \quad}$

$x^2 + 4x + 9 = \qquad +5$

$\underline{\quad -5 \qquad\qquad -5 \quad}$

$x^2 + 4x + 4 = 0$

$(x+2)(x+2) = 0$

$x+2 = 0 \qquad x+2 = 0$

$x = -2 \qquad\quad x = -2$

$y = 2x + 5$

$y = 2(-2) + 5$

$y = -4 + 5$

$y = 1$

solution is $(-2, 1)$

⑦ $x^2 - 3x + 2 = x^2 - 4x + 3$

$\underline{\quad -x^2 \qquad\quad -x^2 \quad}$

$-3x + 2 = \qquad -4x + 3$

$\underline{\quad +4x \qquad\qquad +4x \quad}$

$1x + 2 = \qquad\qquad +3$

$\underline{\quad -3 \qquad\qquad\quad -3 \quad}$

$x - 1 = 0$

$x = 1$

$y = x^2 - 4x + 3$

$y = 1^2 - 4(1) + 3$

$y = 1 \;\; -4 + 3$

$y = 0$

solution is $(1, 0)$

⑥ $x^2 - 2x + 1 = 3x - 5$

$\underline{\quad -3x \qquad -3x \quad}$

$x^2 - 5x + 1 = \qquad -5$

$\underline{\quad +5 \qquad\qquad +5 \quad}$

$x^2 - 5x + 6 = 0$

$(x-2)(x-3) = 0$

$x - 2 = 0 \qquad x - 3 = 0$

$x = 2 \qquad\qquad x = 3$

$y = 3x - 5 \qquad\qquad y = 3x - 5$

$y = 3(2) - 5 \qquad\quad y = 3(3) - 5$

$y = 6 - 5 \qquad\qquad y = 9 - 5$

$y = 1 \qquad\qquad\qquad y = 4$

solutions are $(2, 1)$ and $(3, 4)$

⑧ $x^2 - 9 = -x^2 + 9$

$\underline{\quad +x^2 \qquad\quad +x^2 \quad}$

$2x^2 - 9 = \qquad +9$

$\underline{\quad -9 \qquad\qquad -9 \quad}$

$2x^2 - 18 = 0$

$2(x^2 - 9) = 0$

$2(x^2 - 9) = 0$

$2(x+3)(x-3) = 0$

$x + 3 = 0 \qquad x - 3 = 0$

$x = -3 \qquad\quad x = 3$

$y = -x^2 + 9 \qquad\quad y = -x^2 + 9$

$y = -(-3)^2 + 9 \qquad y = -(3)^2 + 9$

$y = -9 + 9 \qquad\qquad y = -9 + 9$

$y = 0 \qquad\qquad\qquad y = 0$

solutions are $(-3, 0)$ and $(3, 0)$

⑨ $x^2 + 4x + 3 = 4x + 8$
$ -4x \qquad\quad -4x$
$x^2 + 3 = + 8$
$ -8 \qquad\quad -8$
$x^2 - 5 = 0$

$a = 1, b = 0, c = -5$

$x = \dfrac{-0 \pm \sqrt{0^2 - 4(1)(-5)}}{2(1)}$

$x = \dfrac{0 \pm \sqrt{20}}{2}$

$x = \dfrac{\pm \sqrt{4 \cdot 5}}{2}$

$x = \dfrac{\pm 2\sqrt{5}}{2}$ or $\pm\sqrt{5}$

$y = 4x + 8 \qquad y = 4x + 8$
$y = 4(\sqrt{5}) + 8 \quad y = 4(-\sqrt{5}) + 8$
$y = 4\sqrt{5} + 8 \qquad y = -4\sqrt{5} + 8$
solutions are
$(\sqrt{5}, 4\sqrt{5} + 8)$ & $(-\sqrt{5}, -4\sqrt{5} + 8)$

⑩ $x^2 - 3 = x - 6$
$x^2 + 0x - 3 = x - 6$
$ -x \qquad -x$
$x^2 - x - 3 = -6$
$ +6 \qquad +6$
$x^2 - x + 3 = 0$

$a = 1, b = -1, c = 3$

$x = \dfrac{+1 \pm \sqrt{(-1)^2 - 4(1)(3)}}{2(1)}$

$x = \dfrac{+1 \pm \sqrt{1 - 12}}{2}$

$x = \dfrac{+1 \pm \sqrt{-11}}{2}$

These are not real so there are no real simultaneous solutions

⑪ $3x^2 + 1 = 7x - 3$
$3x^2 + 0x + 1 = 7x - 3$
$ -7x \qquad -7x$
$3x^2 - 7x + 1 = -3$
$ +3 \qquad +3$
$3x^2 - 7x + 4 = 0$

$(3x - 4)(x - 1) = 0$
$3x - 4 = 0 \qquad x - 1 = 0$
$3x = 4 \qquad\quad x = 1$
$x = \dfrac{4}{3}$

$y = 7x - 3 \qquad\qquad y = 7x - 3$
$y = 7\left(\dfrac{4}{3}\right) - 3 \qquad y = 7(1) - 3$
$ \qquad\qquad\qquad y = 7 - 3$
$y = \dfrac{28}{3} - \dfrac{9}{3} \qquad\quad y = 4$
$y = \dfrac{19}{3}$ or $6\dfrac{1}{3}$

solutions are $\left(\dfrac{4}{3}, \dfrac{19}{3}\right)$ and $(1, 4)$

or $\left(1\dfrac{1}{3}, 6\dfrac{1}{3}\right)$ and $(1, 4)$

Additional Exercises

Find all the simultaneous solutions of each pair of equations algebraically.

1. $y = x^2 - 7x + 10$
   $y = x + 3$
2. $y = x^2 - 4x + 4$
   $y = x - 2$
3. $y = x^2 - 2$
   $y = x + 4$
4. $y = x^2 - 4$
   $y = 2x - 1$
5. $y = x^2 + 4x + 5$
   $y = 2x + 4$
6. $y = x^2 - 3x - 4$
   $y = x - 8$
7. $y = x^2 - 6x + 5$
   $y = x^2 - 7x + 6$
8. $y = x^2 - 16$
   $y = -x^2 + 16$
9. $y = x^2 + 2x + 1$
   $y = 2x + 3$
10. $y = x^2 - 2$
    $y = x - 3$
11. $y = 2x^2 - 5$
    $y = x + 1$

Lesson 7

Perimeters and Areas

In business, science, industry and other areas, we frequently use equations to express relationships which do not change. Such equations are called **formulas**.

Perimeter

The distance around a flat shape is called its **perimeter**. If we want to enclose a piece of land with a fence, we need to know the perimeter of the land. The figure below represents a piece of land that has five sides. The lengths of the sides are a, b, c, d and e. See Figure 1.

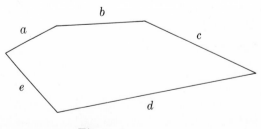

Figure 1

We get the perimeter by adding the length of the sides. If we let P stand for the perimeter, we can write the following formula for the perimeter of this five-sided figure.

$$P = a + b + c + d + e$$

EXAMPLE 1 Use a formula to find the perimeter of the figure shown.

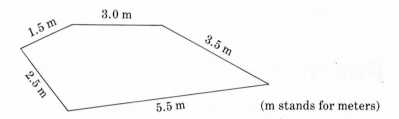

(m stands for meters)

The formula for the perimeter of a five-sided figure is

$$P = a + b + c + d + e$$

We plug in the lengths of the sides for a, b, c, d and e.

$$P = a + b + c + d + e$$

becomes $P = 1.5 + 3.0 + 3.5 + 5.5 + 2.5$

or $\quad\quad P = 16.0$

So the perimeter is 16.0 meters or 16 m.

Here are some formulas for finding the distance around particular flat shapes. These formulas are used frequently.

Perimeter of a rectangle

$$P = 2l + 2w$$

where l is length and w is width.

rectangle

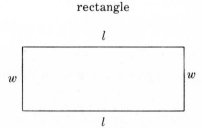

Perimeter of a square

$$P = 4s$$

where s is the length of one side.

square

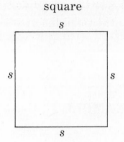

Perimeter of a triangle

$$P = a + b + c$$

where a, b and c are the lengths of the sides.

triangle

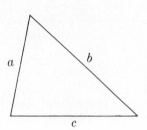

Circumference of a circle   The distance around a circle is called its **circumference**. We use C to stand for the circumference. There are two formulas that are used.

(1) $C = 2\pi r$

circle

where π, an irrational number, is approximately 3.14 (π is pronounced *pie*.), and where r is the distance from the center of the circle to its rim. This distance is called the **radius** of the circle.

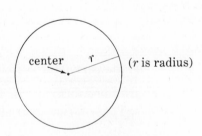

(r is radius)

(2) $C = \pi d$

where π is approximately 3.14, and where d is the distance across the circle through its center. This distance is called the **diameter** of the circle. The diameter is twice as long as the radius.

r is radius
d is diameter

So $d = 2r$.

EXAMPLE 2   A rectangular plot of land is 60 ft by 100 ft. How much fencing is needed to enclose it?

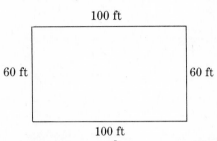

100 ft

60 ft

60 ft

100 ft

We need to find the distance around this rectangle, which is its perimeter. The formula for the perimeter of a rectangle is

$$P = 2l + 2w$$

We plug in 100 for l and 60 for w.

$$P = 2l + 2w$$
becomes $P = 2(100) + 2(60)$
$$P = 200 + 120$$
$$P = 320$$

So 320 ft of fencing is needed to enclose this rectangular plot.

EXAMPLE 3   Each side of a square rug is 3.5 meters. How much material is needed to bind the edges?

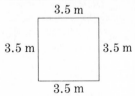

3.5 m

3.5 m

3.5 m

3.5 m

We need to find the distance around the rug, which is its perimeter. The formula for the perimeter of a square is

$$P = 4s$$

We plug in 3.5 for s.

$$P = 4s$$
becomes $P = 4(3.5)$
$$P = 14.0$$

So 14 meters of material or 14 m is needed to bind the edges of the rug.

EXAMPLE 4   The figure below shows the distances between cities. A salesman who lives in City A travels to City B and then to City C and returns home. How far has he traveled?

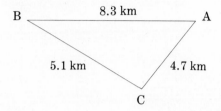

We need to find the distance around the triangle, which is its perimeter. The formula for the perimeter of a triangle is

$$P = a + b + c$$

We plug in 8.3 for a, 5.1 for b and 4.7 for c.

$$P = a + b + c$$
becomes $P = 8.3 + 5.1 + 4.7$
$$P = 18.1$$

So the distance the salesman has travelled is 18.1 km.

EXAMPLE 5   A circular shaped swimming pool has a radius of 32 ft. How many feet of fencing is required to enclose it? (Use 3.14 for π.)

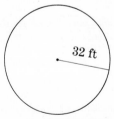

We need to find the distance around the pool, which is the circumference of the circle. The formula we use is

$$C = 2\pi r$$

We plug in 3.14 for π and 32 for r.

$$C = 2\pi r$$
becomes $C = 2(3.14)(32)$
$$C = 200.96$$

So 200.96 ft of fencing is needed to enclose the pool.

EXAMPLE 6 The diameter of a circular running track is 65 meters. How far would a runner travel if he ran three times around the track? (Use 3.14 for π.)

We need to find the distance around the circle, which is its circumference, and then multiply by three. Since we are given the diameter of the circle, the formula we use is

$$C = \pi d$$

We plug in 3.14 for π and 65 for d.

$$C = \pi d$$
becomes $C = 3.14(65)$
$$C = 204.1$$

Since the runner goes three times around the track, we multiply 204.1 by 3.

$$3(204.1) = 612.3$$

So the runner travels 612.3 meters.

Area

The amount of space inside the perimeter of a flat shape is called its area. For instance, the area of a one-inch square is 1 square inch.

1 in

1 in   area = 1 sq in or 1 in²

The area of a one-foot square is 1 square foot.

1 ft

1 ft   area = 1 sq ft or 1 ft²

The area of a one-meter square is 1 square meter.

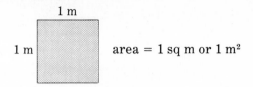

The area of a one-yard square is 1 square yard.

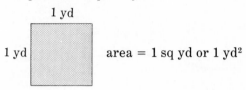

Area is always expressed in square units.

If we want to know how much carpeting is needed to completely cover the floor of a room, we need to know the area of a room. Consider a room that measures 3 yards by 4 yards.

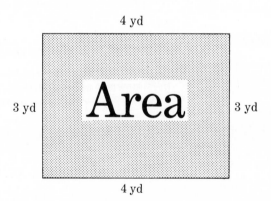

The area of this room is the number of one-square-yard pieces that fit inside the room.

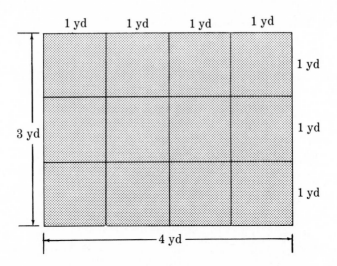

Since 12 square-yard pieces fit inside the room (which measures 3 yards by 4 yards), the area is 12 square yards or 12 yd². We would need 12 square yards of carpeting to cover the room.

Instead of cutting a space into square boxes, we can use formulas to find area. Here are some formulas that are used frequently.

Area of a rectangle

$$A = lw$$

where l is length and w is width.

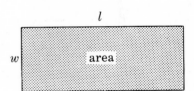

Area of a square

$$A = s^2$$

where s is the length of one side.

Area of a triangle

$$A = \frac{1}{2}bh$$

where b is the base and h is the height.

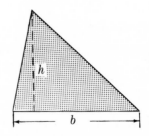

Area of a circle

$$A = \pi r^2$$

where π is approximately 3.14 and r is the radius.

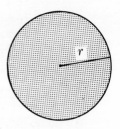

EXAMPLE 7   How much linoleum is needed to completely cover a rectangular floor which measures 3 yards by 4 yards?

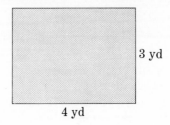

3 yd

4 yd

We need to find the floorspace of the room, which is its area. The formula for the area of a rectangle is

$$A = lw$$

We plug in 4 for l and 3 for w.

$$A = lw$$
becomes $A = (4)(3)$
$$A = 12$$

So 12 yd² of linoleum are needed for this room.

EXAMPLE 8   A square plot of land has an area of 6400 ft². Find the length of a side of the plot of land.

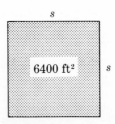

s

6400 ft² s

The formula for the area of a square is

$$A = s^2$$

We plug in 6400 for A.

$$A = s^2$$
becomes $6400 = s^2$
$$\pm 80 = s$$

Since no side can have a negative length, $s = 80$. So the side of this plot of land is 80 ft.

EXAMPLE 9   A piece of land has the shape of a triangle with the dimensions shown. Find the area of this land.

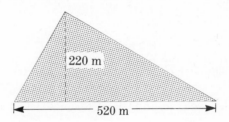

The formula for the area of a triangle is

$$A = \frac{1}{2}bh$$

We plug in 520 for b and 220 for h.

$$A = \frac{1}{2}bh$$
becomes $A = \frac{1}{2}(520)(220)$
$$A = 57{,}200$$

So the area of the land is 57,200 m².

EXAMPLE 10   Find the difference in area between a round table top with radius 4 feet and one with radius 5 feet. (Use 3.14 for π.)

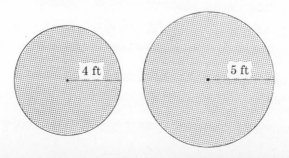

We use the formula $A = \pi r^2$ to find the area of each table top. For the table with radius 4 ft

$$A = \pi r^2$$
becomes $A = 3.14(4)(4)$
$$A = 50.24$$

So the area of the 4-ft-radius table top is 50.24 ft².

For the table with radius 5 ft

$$A = \pi r^2$$
becomes $A = 3.14(5)(5)$
$$A = 78.50$$

So the area of the 5-ft-radius table top is 78.50 ft².

We subtract the areas to find the difference.

$$
\begin{array}{r}
78.50 \text{ ft}^2 \\
-50.24 \text{ ft}^2 \\
\hline
28.26 \text{ ft}^2
\end{array}
$$

So the 5-ft-radius table top has an area which is 28.26 square feet larger than the table top with a 4-ft radius.

EXAMPLE 11   Which has the greater area, a circle with diameter of 50 centimeters or a 49-centimeter square? (Use 3.14 for π.)

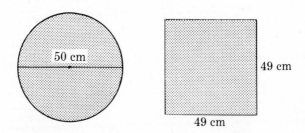

To find the area of the circle, we use the formula $A = \pi r^2$. To use this formula, we need to know r, the radius of the circle. Since the diameter is 50 cm, the radius, which is one half the diameter, is 25 cm. We plug in 3.14 for π and 25 for r.

$$A = \pi r^2$$
becomes $\quad A = 3.14(25)(25)$
$$A = 1962.5$$

So the area of the circle is 1962.5 cm².

To find the area of the square, we use the formula $A = s^2$. We plug in 49 for s.

$$A = s^2$$
becomes $\quad A = (49)(49)$
$$A = 2401$$

So the area of the square is 2401 cm².

The area of a 49-centimeter square is larger than the area of a circle with diameter of 50 centimeters.

Exercises

What is the perimeter of each of the following figures?

1.

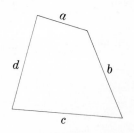

3.

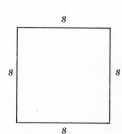

2.

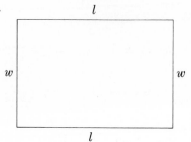

4.

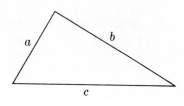

5.

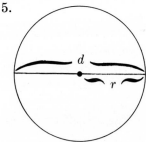

Find the perimeter of each of the following figures. Include units in your answer. Use 3.14 as an approximation for π.

6.   a rectangle 25 cm long and 15 cm wide

7.   a square with side 3 yards

8.   a triangle with each side 4 inches

9.   a circle with a radius of 8 m

10.   a circle with a diameter of 4 feet

11.   a rectangle 4.5 feet long and 3.5 feet wide

12.   a square with side 6.5 cm

13.   a triangle with sides $3\frac{2}{3}$ feet, $6\frac{1}{3}$ feet and $5\frac{1}{3}$ feet

14.   a circle with a radius of 3 inches

15.   a circle with a diameter of 7 km

What is the area of each of the following figures?

16.

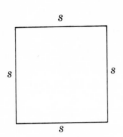

18.

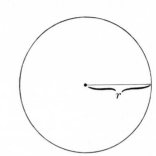

17.

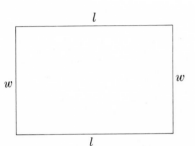

19.

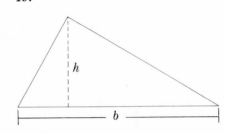

Find the area of each of the following figures. Include units in your answer. Use 3.14 as an approximation for π.

20. a square with side 5 feet
21. a rectangle 25 cm long and 15 cm wide
22. a circle with a radius of 12 inches
23. a circle with a diameter of 40 feet
24. a triangle with base 15 cm and perpendicular height 8 cm
25. a square with side 4.5 m
26. a rectangle 14.2 cm long and 12.4 cm wide
27. a circle with a radius of $3\frac{1}{2}$ feet
28. a circle with a diameter of 2.5 yards
29. a triangle with base 10 inches and perpendicular height 7 inches

Do the following word problems.

30. A rectangular plot of land is 80 feet by 120 feet. How much fencing is needed to enclose it? What is the area of this plot of land?

31. Each side of a square rug is 8.5 m. How much material is needed to bind the edges? What is the area of this rug?

32. A circular shaped swimming pool has a radius of 16 feet. How many feet of fencing is required to enclose it? What is the area of the bottom of the pool? (Use 3.14 for π.)

33. A piece of land has the shape of a triangle with the dimensions shown below. Find the perimeter and area of this piece of land.

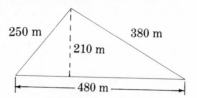

34. A rectangular garden plot needs to be 8 feet wide and should be 144 square feet in area. How long should it be?

35. Find the difference in area between two small pizza pies, each with radius 6 inches, and one large pizza pie with radius 8 inches. (Use 3.14 for π.)

36. A rectangular parking lot is 90 feet by 120 feet. If each parking space is 6 feet by 10 feet, how many cars can the lot hold?

Answers to Exercises

(1.) $p = a + b + c + d$

(2.) $p = 2l + 2w$

(3.) $p = 4s$

(4.) $p = a + b + c$

(5.) $C = 2\pi r$ or $C = \pi d$

(The perimeter of a circle is called the circumference)

(6.) $p = 2l + 2w$
$p = 2(25) + 2(15)$
$p = 50 + 30$
$p = 80$ cm

(7.) $p = 4s$
$p = 4(3)$
$p = 12$ yd

(8.) $p = a + b + c$
$p = 4 + 4 + 4$
$p = 12$ in

(9.) $C = 2\pi r$
$C = 2(3.14)(8)$
$C = 50.24$ m

(10.) $C = \pi d$
$C = (3.14)(4)$
$C = 12.56$ ft

(11.) $p = 2l + 2w$
$p = 2(4.5) + 2(3.5)$
$p = 9 + 7$
$p = 16$ ft

(12.) $p = 4s$
$p = 4(6.5)$
$p = 26$ cm

(13.) $p = a + b + c$
$p = 3\frac{2}{3} + 6\frac{1}{3} + 5\frac{1}{3}$
$p = (3 + 6 + 5) + \left(\frac{2}{3} + \frac{1}{3} + \frac{1}{3}\right)$
$p = 14 + \frac{4}{3}$
$p = 15\frac{1}{3}$ ft

(14.) $C = 2\pi r$
$C = 2(3.14)(3)$
$C = 18.84$ in

(15.) $C = \pi d$
$C = (3.14)(7)$
$C = 21.98$ km

(16.) $A = s^2$

(17.) $A = l\,w$

(18.) $A = \pi r^2$

(19.) $A = \frac{1}{2}\,b\,h$

(20.) $A = s^2$
$A = (5)^2$
$A = 25\ ft^2$

(21.) $A = l\,w$
$A = (25)(15)$
$A = 375\ cm^2$

(22.) $A = \pi r^2$
$A = (3.14)(12)^2$
$A = (3.14)(144)$
$A = 452.16\ in^2$

(23.) $A = \pi r^2$
$A = (3.14)(20)^2$
$A = (3.14)(400)$
$A = 1256\ ft^2$

(24.) $A = \frac{1}{2}\,b\,h$
$A = \frac{1}{2}(15)(8)$
$A = 60\ cm^2$

(25.) $A = s^2$
$A = (4.5)^2$
$A = 20.25\ in^2$

(26.) $A = l\,w$
$A = (14.2)(12.4)$
$A = 176.08\ cm^2$

(27.) $A = \pi r^2$
$A = (3.14)(3.5)^2$
$A = 38.465\ ft^2$

(28.) $A = \pi r^2$
$A = (3.14)(1.25)^2$
$A = 4.90625\ yd^2$

(29.) $A = \frac{1}{2}\,b\,h$
$A = \frac{1}{2}(10)(7)$
$A = 35\ in^2$

(30.) $p = 2l + 2w$
$p = 2(80) + 2(120)$
$p = 160 + 240$
$p = 400\ ft$
$A = l\,w$
$A = (80)(120)$
$A = 9600\ ft^2$

(31.) $p = 4s$
$p = 4(8.5)$
$p = 34 \, m$
$A = s^2$
$A = (8.5)^2$
$A = 72.25 \, m^2$

(32.) $C = 2\pi r$
$C = 2(3.14)(16)$
$C = 100.48 \, ft$
$A = \pi r^2$
$A = (3.14)(16)^2$
$A = (3.14)(256)$
$A = 803.84 \, ft^2$

(33) $p = a + b + c$
$p = 250 + 380 + 480$
$p = 1110 \, m$
$A = \frac{1}{2} b h$
$A = \frac{1}{2}(480)(210)$

$A = 50400 \, m^2$

(34.) $A = l w$
$144 = l(8)$
$\dfrac{144}{8} = \dfrac{l \cdot 8}{8}$
$18 = l$
$l = 18 \, ft$

(35.) $A = \pi r^2$
$A = (3.14)(6)^2$
$A = (3.14)(36)$
$A = 113.04 \, in^2$
$A = \pi r^2$
$A = (3.14)(8)^2$
$A = (3.14)(64)$
$A = 200.96 \, in^2$

area of 2 small pizzas is $226.08 \, in^2$.
area of 1 large pizza is $200.96 \, in^2$
$$\begin{array}{r} 226.08 \\ -200.96 \\ \hline 25.12 \, in^2 \end{array}$$

Difference is $25.12 \, in^2$

(36.) area of parking space
$A = l w$
$A = 6(10)$
$A = 60 \, ft^2$
area of lot
$A = l w$
$A = 90(120)$
$A = 10800 \, ft^2$

$\dfrac{10800}{60} = 180 \, cars$

Additional Exercises

Find the perimeter of each of the following figures. Include units in each answer. Use 3.14 as an approximation for π.

1.

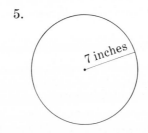

3.0 m

1.0 m

2.0 m

2.5 m

1.5 m

3.

2.7 m

2.7 m   2.7 m

2.7 m

2.

$4\frac{1}{2}$ feet

3 feet   3 feet

$4\frac{1}{2}$ feet

4.

3 yards

$6\frac{1}{2}$ yards

8 yards

5.

7 inches

Find the perimeter of each of the following figures. Include units in each answer. Use 3.14 as an approximation for π.

6.   a rectangle 34 feet long and 14 feet wide

7.   a square with side 4 cm

8.   a triangle with each side 8 inches

9.   a circle with a radius of 12 m

10. a circle with a diameter of 5 km

11. a rectangle 3.4 inches long and 2.7 inches wide

12. a square with side 4.8 cm

13. a triangle with sides $2\frac{1}{4}$ yards, $3\frac{3}{4}$ yards and $4\frac{1}{4}$ yards

14. a circle with a radius of 5 m

15. a circle with a diameter of 9 feet

Find the area of each of the following figures. Include units in each answer. Use 3.14 as an approximation for π.

16.

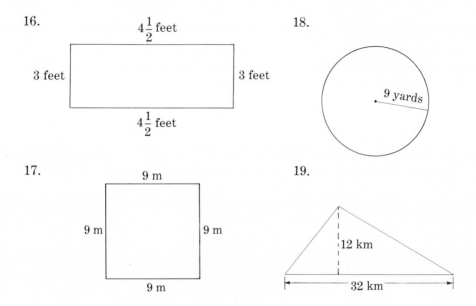

18.

17.
9 m

19.

Find the area of each of the following figures. Include units in each answer. Use 3.14 as an approximation for π.

20.   a square with side 7 inches
21.   a rectangle 43 cm long and 32 cm wide
22.   a circle with a radius of 5 feet
23.   a circle with a diameter of 27 inches
24.   a triangle with base 12 m and perpendicular height 9 m
25.   a square with side 5.2 cm
26.   a rectangle 11.5 km long and 9.3 km wide
27.   a circle with a radius of $4\frac{1}{2}$ inches
28.   a circle with a diameter of 4.5 yards
29.   a triangle with base 11 inches and perpendicular height 8 inches

Do the following word problems.
30.   A rug is 9 feet by 12 feet. How much material is needed to bind the edges? What is the area of this rug?

31.   A circular running track has a radius of 40 meters. How far would a runner travel if she ran two times around the track? (Use 3.14 for π.)

32.   A square mirror has each edge of length 9 inches. What is the perimeter of the mirror? What is the area of the mirror?

33. The figure below shows the distance between three cities. A salesman who lives in city A travels to city B and then to city C and then returns home. How far has he travelled?

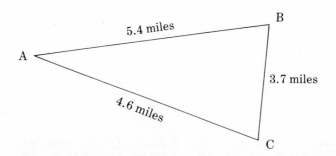

34. A rectangular parking lot is 84,000 square feet. If the width is 240 feet, what is the length of the parking lot?

35. Two flags each have widths of 17 inches. The length of one flag is 25 inches, and the length of the other flag is 28 inches. Find the area of each of the flags and find the difference in area between the two flags.

36. Find the difference in area between a square rug with side 8 feet and a circular rug with diameter 9 feet.

Lesson 8

Formulas and Applications

When a triangle has a square corner, it is called a **right triangle**. Figure 1 shows some right triangles. In each triangle, we show a box to indicate the square corner (**right angle**). The side opposite each right angle is the longest side of the triangle and is called the **hypotenuse**. The other sides are called **legs**.

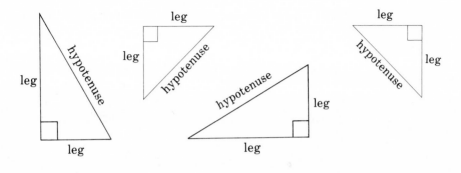

Figure 1

The formula which gives the relationship between the length of the hypotenuse of any right triangle and the lengths of its two legs is called the **Pythagorean Theorem**

$$c^2 = a^2 + b^2$$

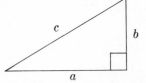

where a and b are the lengths of the legs and c is the length of the hypotenuse.

EXAMPLE 1 In a right triangle, the length of one leg is 3, the length of the other leg is 4. Find the hypotenuse.

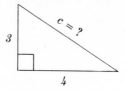

We use the Pythagorean Theorem $c^2 = a^2 + b^2$ to find the hypotenuse c. We plug in 3 for a and 4 for b.

$$c^2 = a^2 + b^2$$
becomes $c^2 = 3^2 + 4^2$
$$c^2 = 9 + 16$$
$$c^2 = 25$$
$$c = \pm 5$$

Since the length of the hypotenuse cannot be negative, we choose the positive number. So the hypotenuse is 5.

EXAMPLE 2 One leg of a right triangle is 5 and its hypotenuse is 13. Find the length of the other leg.

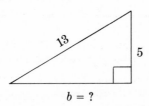

We use the Pythagorean Theorem $c^2 = a^2 + b^2$. We plug in 5 for a and 13 for c.

$$
\begin{array}{rl}
c^2 = & a^2 + b^2 \\
\text{becomes} \quad 13^2 = & 5^2 + b^2 \\
169 = & 25 + b^2 \\
\text{Add } -25 \quad \underline{-25} & \underline{-25} \\
144 = & b^2 \\
\pm 12 = & b
\end{array}
$$

Since the length of a leg cannot be negative, we choose the positive number. So the other leg is 12.

EXAMPLE 3   A 15-ft ladder leans against a wall, 12 ft up from the ground. How far from the building is the bottom of the ladder?

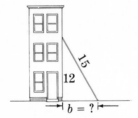

Since a right triangle is formed, we will use the Pythagorean Theorem $c^2 = a^2 + b^2$. We plug in 12 for a and 15 for c.

$$
\begin{array}{rl}
c^2 = & a^2 + b^2 \\
\text{becomes} \quad 15^2 = & 12^2 + b^2 \\
225 = & 144 + b^2 \\
\text{Add } -144 \quad \underline{-144} & \underline{-144} \\
81 = & b^2 \\
\pm 9 = & b
\end{array}
$$

Since b cannot be negative, we choose the positive number. Thus the distance from the building to the bottom of the ladder is 9 ft.

The formula for the area of a rectangle is $A = lw$. This formula gives us the area in terms of length and width. Suppose we want a formula for the width of a rectangle in terms of length and area. We can use algebra to get this formula. We start with the formula we already have: $A = lw$. We want w by itself on one side of the equation; that is, we want to solve the equation for w.

$$A = lw$$

Divide by l.

$$\frac{A}{l} = \frac{\cancel{l}w}{\cancel{l}}$$

$$\frac{A}{l} = w$$

So the formula we want is $w = \dfrac{A}{l}$.

EXAMPLE 4   The formula for the circumference of a circle is $C = 2\pi r$. Use this formula to find a formula for r.

We want to solve for r. We start with the formula we already have.

$$C = 2\pi r$$

Divide by 2π.

$$\frac{C}{2\pi} = \frac{\cancel{2\pi}r}{\cancel{2\pi}}$$

$$\frac{C}{2\pi} = r$$

So the formula we want is $r = \dfrac{C}{2\pi}$

EXAMPLE 5   The formula for the perimeter of a rectangle is $P = 2l + 2w$. Use this formula to find a formula for w.

We want to solve for w. We start with the formula we already have.

$$
\begin{array}{rccc}
 & P = & 2l + & 2w \\
\text{Add } -2l & & -2l & -2l \\
\hline
 & P - 2l = & & 2w
\end{array}
$$

Divide by 2.

$$\frac{P - 2l}{2} = \frac{\cancel{2}w}{\cancel{2}}$$

$$\frac{P - 2l}{2} = w$$

So the formula we want is $w = \dfrac{P - 2l}{2}$.

EXAMPLE 6   The Pythagorean Theorem $c^2 = a^2 + b^2$ gives the relationship between the length of the hypotenuse c of a right triangle, and the lengths of the two legs a and b. Use this formula to find a formula for b.

We want to solve for b. We start with the formula we know.

$$
\begin{array}{rcl}
c^2 & = & a^2 + b^2 \\
\text{Add } -a^2 \quad -a^2 & & -a^2 \\
\hline
c^2 - a^2 & = & b^2 \\
\pm\sqrt{c^2 - a^2} & = & b
\end{array}
$$

But the length of a leg cannot be negative, so the formula we want is $b = \sqrt{c^2 - a^2}$.

EXAMPLE 7   The formula for conversion of Celsius temperature to Fahrenheit temperature is $F = \dfrac{9}{5}C + 32$. Use this formula to find a formula for C.

We want to solve for C. We start with the formula we have.

$$F = \frac{9}{5}C + 32$$

Add -32
$$
\begin{array}{rcl}
-32 & & -32 \\
\hline
F - 32 & = & \dfrac{9}{5}C
\end{array}
$$

Multiply by 5.

$$5(F - 32) = \cancel{5}\left(\frac{9}{\cancel{5}}C\right)$$

Divide by 9.

$$\frac{5(F - 32)}{9} = \frac{\cancel{9}C}{\cancel{9}}$$

$$\frac{5}{9}\left(F - 32\right) = C$$

So the formula we want is $C = \dfrac{5}{9}\left(F - 32\right)$.

EXAMPLE 8   Solve the equation $4x - a = 3x + b$ for x in terms of a and b.

We want to solve for x. We head for "$x =$ ".

$$
\begin{array}{lrr}
 & 4x - a = & 3x + b \\
\text{Add} - 3x & -3x & -3x \\
\hline
 & x - a = & b \\
\text{Add} +a & +a & +a \\
\hline
 & x = & b + a
\end{array}
$$

So the equation we want is $x = b + a$.

EXAMPLE 9   The formula for the area of a circle is $A = \pi r^2$, where r is the radius. Use this formula to find a formula for r.

We want to solve for r. We start with the formula we already have.

$$A = \pi r^2$$

Divide by π.

$$\frac{A}{\pi} = \frac{\cancel{\pi}r^2}{\cancel{\pi}}$$

$$\frac{A}{\pi} = r^2$$

$$\pm\sqrt{\frac{A}{\pi}} = r$$

But the length of the radius cannot be negative, so the formula we want is $r = \sqrt{\dfrac{A}{\pi}}$.

EXAMPLE 10   The formula for the gravitational force between two planets is given by $F = \dfrac{GmM}{d^2}$.   Use this formula to find a formula for G. Note that m and M are different symbols.

We want to solve for G. We start with the formula we already have.

$$F = \frac{GmM}{d^2}$$

Multiply by d^2.

$$d^2F = d^2\left(\frac{GmM}{d^2}\right)$$

Divide by mM.

$$\frac{d^2F}{mM} = \frac{GmM}{mM}$$

So the formula we want is $G = \dfrac{d^2F}{mM}$.

EXAMPLE 11   A formula used in banking is $A = P + PRT$. Use this formula to find a formula for P.

We want to solve for P. We start with the formula we already have.

$$A = P + PRT$$

Factor the right side.

$$A = P(1 + RT)$$

Divide by $(1 + RT)$.

$$\frac{A}{(1 + RT)} = \frac{P\cancel{(1 + RT)}}{\cancel{(1 + RT)}}$$

$$\frac{A}{1 + RT} = P$$

So the formula we want is $P = \dfrac{A}{1 + RT}$.

Exercises

In each of the following exercises the lengths of two sides of a right triangle are given. Find the length of the third side.

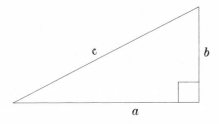

1. $a = 4, b = 3$
2. $a = 6, b = 8$
3. $a = 5, b = 5$
4. $a = 2, b = 3$
5. $a = 2, c = 5$
6. $b = 8, c = 17$

Solve each of the following equations for the indicated variables.

7. $A = lw$ solve for l
8. $C = \pi d$ solve for d
9. $P = 2l + 2w$ solve for l
10. $c^2 = a^2 + b^2$ solve for a
11. $ax = bc$ solve for x
12. $A = P + PRT$ solve for T
13. $2a + 3x = b$ solve for x
14. $ax + bx = c$ solve for x
15. $P = 4s$ solve for s

16. $A = \dfrac{1}{2}bh$ solve for b

17. $5x - a = 4x + b$ solve for x
18. $V = lwh$ solve for l

19. $V = \dfrac{1}{3}\pi r^2 h$ solve for h

20. $Br = St$ solve for t

21. $\dfrac{A}{B} = \dfrac{C}{D}$ solve for D

22. $S = \dfrac{1}{2}gt^2$ solve for g

23. $bx = cx + bc$ solve for x

24. $\dfrac{1}{a} + \dfrac{1}{b} = \dfrac{1}{c}$ solve for c

25. $G = \dfrac{cD}{AB}$ solve for c

Answers to Exercises

(1.)
$$a^2 + b^2 = c^2$$
$$4^2 + 3^2 = c^2$$
$$16 + 9 = c^2$$
$$25 = c^2$$
$$5 = c$$

(6.)
$$a^2 + b^2 = c^2$$
$$a^2 + 8^2 = 17^2$$
$$a^2 + 64 = 289$$
$$a^2 = 225$$
$$a = 15$$

(2.)
$$a^2 + b^2 = c^2$$
$$6^2 + 8^2 = c^2$$
$$36 + 64 = c^2$$
$$100 = c^2$$
$$10 = c$$

(7.)
$$A = \ell w$$
$$\frac{A}{w} = \frac{\ell \cancel{w}}{\cancel{w}}$$
$$\frac{A}{w} = \ell$$

(3.)
$$a^2 + b^2 = c^2$$
$$5^2 + 5^2 = c^2$$
$$25 + 25 = c^2$$
$$50 = c^2$$
$$\sqrt{50} = c$$
$$c = \sqrt{5 \cdot 5 \cdot 2}$$
$$c = 5\sqrt{2}$$

(8.)
$$C = \pi d$$
$$\frac{C}{\pi} = \frac{\cancel{\pi} d}{\cancel{\pi}}$$
$$\frac{C}{\pi} = d$$

(4.)
$$a^2 + b^2 = c^2$$
$$2^2 + 3^2 = c^2$$
$$4 + 9 = c^2$$
$$13 = c^2$$
$$\sqrt{13} = c$$

(9.)
$$p = 2\ell + 2w$$
$$\underline{-2w \qquad\quad -2w}$$
$$p - 2w = 2\ell$$
$$\frac{p - 2w}{2} = \frac{\cancel{2}\ell}{\cancel{2}}$$
$$\frac{p - 2w}{2} = \ell$$

(5.)
$$a^2 + b^2 = c^2$$
$$2^2 + b^2 = 5^2$$
$$4 + b^2 = 25$$
$$b^2 = 21$$
$$b = \sqrt{21}$$

(10.) $c^2 = a^2 + b^2$

$$\frac{-b^2 \qquad -b^2}{c^2 - b^2 = a^2}$$

$$\pm\sqrt{c^2 - b^2} = a$$

For the Pythagorean Theorem, length of a leg cannot be negative so $a = \sqrt{c^2 - b^2}$

(11.) $ax = bc$

$$\frac{\cancel{a}x}{\cancel{a}} = \frac{bc}{a}$$

$$x = \frac{bc}{a}$$

(12.) $A = p + pRT$

$$\frac{-p \qquad -p}{A - p = pRT}$$

$$\frac{A - p}{pR} = \frac{\cancel{pR}T}{\cancel{pR}}$$

$$\frac{A - p}{pR} = T$$

(13.) $2a + 3x = b$

$$\frac{-2a \qquad\qquad -2a}{3x = b - 2a}$$

$$\frac{\cancel{3}x}{\cancel{3}} = \frac{b - 2a}{3}$$

$$x = \frac{b - 2a}{3}$$

(14.) $ax + bx = c$

$x(a + b) = c$

$$\frac{x\cancel{(a+b)}}{\cancel{a+b}} = \frac{c}{a+b}$$

$$x = \frac{c}{a+b}$$

(15.) $p = 4s$

$$\frac{p}{4} = \frac{\cancel{4}s}{\cancel{4}}$$

$$\frac{p}{4} = s$$

(16.) $A = \frac{1}{2}bh$

$2(A) = \cancel{2}\left(\frac{1}{\cancel{2}}bh\right)$

$2A = bh$

$$\frac{2A}{h} = \frac{b\cancel{h}}{\cancel{h}}$$

$$\frac{2A}{h} = b$$

(17.) $5x - a = 4x + b$

$$\frac{-4x \qquad\qquad -4x}{x - a = b}$$

$$\frac{+a \qquad +a}{x = b + a}$$

(18.) $V = \ell w h$

$\dfrac{V}{wh} = \dfrac{\ell \cancel{w} \cancel{h}}{\cancel{w} \cancel{h}}$

$\dfrac{V}{wh} = \ell$

(19.) $V = \frac{1}{3} \pi r^2 h$

$3(V) = \cancel{3}\left(\frac{1}{\cancel{3}} \pi r^2 h\right)$

$3V = \pi r^2 h$

$\dfrac{3V}{\pi r^2} = \dfrac{\cancel{\pi} \cancel{r^2} h}{\cancel{\pi} \cancel{r^2}}$

$\dfrac{3V}{\pi r^2} = h$

(20.) $Br = St$

$\dfrac{Br}{S} = \dfrac{\cancel{S} t}{\cancel{S}}$

$\dfrac{Br}{S} = t$

(21.) $\dfrac{A}{B} = \dfrac{C}{D}$

$\cancel{B} D\left(\dfrac{A}{\cancel{B}}\right) = B \cancel{D}\left(\dfrac{C}{\cancel{D}}\right)$

$DA = BC$

$\dfrac{D\cancel{A}}{\cancel{A}} = \dfrac{BC}{A}$

$D = \dfrac{BC}{A}$

(22.) $S = \frac{1}{2} g t^2$

$2(S) = \cancel{2}\left(\frac{1}{\cancel{2}} g t^2\right)$

$2S = g t^2$

$\dfrac{2S}{t^2} = \dfrac{g \cancel{t^2}}{\cancel{t^2}}$

$\dfrac{2S}{t^2} = g$

㉓ $bx = cx + bc$

$ \underline{-cx \quad -cx}$

$bx - cx = bc$

$x(b-c) = bc$

$\dfrac{x(b-c)}{b-c} = \dfrac{bc}{b-c}$

$x = \dfrac{bc}{b-c}$

㉔ $\dfrac{1}{a} + \dfrac{1}{b} = \dfrac{1}{c}$

$abc\left(\dfrac{1}{a}\right) + abc\left(\dfrac{1}{b}\right) = abc\left(\dfrac{1}{c}\right)$

$bc + ac = ab$

$c(b+a) = ab$

$\dfrac{c(b+a)}{b+a} = \dfrac{ab}{b+a}$

$c = \dfrac{ab}{b+a}$

㉕ $G = \dfrac{CD}{AB}$

$AB(G) = AB\left(\dfrac{CD}{AB}\right)$

$\dfrac{ABG}{D} = \dfrac{CD}{D}$

$\dfrac{ABG}{D} = C$

Additional Exercises

In each of the following exercises the lengths of two sides of a right triangle are given. Find the length of the third side.

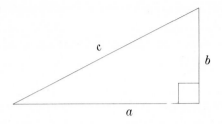

1. $a = 9, b = 12$
2. $a = 5, b = 12$
3. $a = 4, b = 4$
4. $a = 5, b = 8$
5. $a = 3, c = 6$
6. $b = 4, c = 7$

Solve each of the following equations for the indicated variable.

7. $P = a + b + c$ solve for c
8. $E = IR$ solve for R
9. $bx = cd$ solve for x
10. $A = P + PRT$ solve for R
11. $A = \dfrac{1}{2}bh$ solve for b
12. $V = \pi r^2 h$ solve for h
13. $4b + 5x = c$ solve for x
14. $cx + dx = a$ solve for x
15. $7x - 2b = 3x + c$ solve for x
16. $V = lwh$ solve for w
17. $AC = Bg$ solve for g
18. $\dfrac{C}{D} = \dfrac{R}{T}$ solve for T
19. $A = \dfrac{1}{2}h\left(b_1 + b_2\right)$ solve for h
20. $ax = bx + ab$ solve for x
21. $\dfrac{1}{r} = \dfrac{1}{s} + \dfrac{1}{t}$ solve for t

22. $\dfrac{ab}{c} = x + 3$ solve for b

23. $R = \dfrac{aB}{CD}$ solve for a

24. $x + r = b^2$ solve for b

25. $4y - a = \dfrac{3y}{2}$ solve for a

Index